SELF CARE MATTERS
MATTERS
A REVOLUTIONARY'S
APPROACH

By: Anana Johari Harris Parris

Edited By: Kim Brundidge

i

Self Care Agency
470-440-0237
selfcareday.com
selfcareagency.com
sistercarealliance.org

Printed in the United States of America
YBF Publishing, LLC
www.ybfpublishing.com

Self Care Matters: A Revolutionary's Approach First Edition.
Edited by Kim Brundidge

Ordering Information:
Quantity sales. Special discounts are available on quantity purchases by corporations, associations, and others. For details about licensing options for your program or organization, contact the publisher at the contact information listed above.

DEDICATION

This book is dedicated to my great-grandmother, the late Beatrice 'Mombee' Senegal Harris Clues McGee who never stopped praying for our family and for me. The many unsung names of the millions of quiet revolutionaries like my grandmother Annabelle Johnson and her mother, Mombee live in us. Their strength lives on through me. I pray I am honoring her and the sacrifices she made along with the sacrifices of all my ancestors so that I may live, practice self-care and contribute to my community. I still feel you close, praying for me and encouraging me even in my darkest hour. I love you. I miss you. Thank you for loving me.

iv

Acknowledgements

It feels impossible to thank everyone who has helped me thus far in the writing of this book, but I will first thank the Creator for placing every last one of them in my path, lifting up my feet and acknowledging my power when I didn't believe it existed. Those who came before me and fought far worst odds than I, my great grandmother Beatrice Senegal McGee, paternal grandmother Ana Belle Johnson and maternal grandmother Jesse Mae Albert. I give thanks to my father, Herget Dean Sababu Harris and mother Kathleen Ann Assata Albert, my first teachers, for loving me and teaching me the art of cultural self-care when it was hard to be proud of being black in America. To the founders of my first school, Watoto Shule in Washington D.C., thank you instilling the beauty of our culture when there were few options for academic cultural institutions. My siblings Melissa, Crystal, Sekou, Erica and cousin Tricia for always reminding me how far I have come and that I was worthy. My SisterCARE Alliance co-director Letitia Gallman, founding and current members Azania, Candice, Roodgine, Saniyyah, Charity, Kareena, Rosalind, Wan, Sharon, Devi, Brittany P., Toni, Karren, Tayani,

Lauren, Kim, Nia, Noreen, Sunnye, Jasmine, Mama Afiya and Joy for truly lending their time, ears and talents to the inception of this self-care movement.

To my sister friends from school --Michelle, Myra, Cheryl, Trina, Lauren, Keisha, Lisa and Ambre, thank you for loving me like a sister, allowing me to practice what true long-term friendship really means and helping me to learn how to take better care of myself. My angel friends Ragenia, Saniyyah, Nicole, Charity, Kwasida, Dzifa, Natasha, Ayana Perkins, Zalika, Assata, Icesis, Fenyx, Virginia, Kareena, Vonn, Adalia, Rashema, Jewel, Bonnie, Barbara and Ayana C. for swooping in when it was really needed. You all are my spiritual and emotional Self Care Dream Team. To my sister friend and mentor Kim Brundidge for editing the manuscript, encouraging my development into womanhood and simply caring about how I'm doing on the inside, this book would not have happened without you. My brothers who share my love of community service, protection and healing: Brian, Simeon, Jarrod, Gerry, Jabez, David, Mawuli, Jamie, Ted, Sekou, Rob, Marcus, Allen, Eldredge, Khalil, Fabian, Justin and Rashid-- thank you for your fearless authenticity and support for this movement. The women and men of the

Davis Bozeman Law Firm, thank you for encouraging me, making me stronger, expanding my understanding of social justice and caring about me.

To my community partners, activists, board members and campaign committee members-- The Davis Bozeman Law Firm, Self Care Agency, Porter Sanford III Performing Arts & Community Center, Rhythmz and Motion Dance Studio, Balafon West African Dance Company, African Community Centers for Unity and Self Determination, Community Action Coalition, Urban Village Media, The Alaje Group, Giwayen Mata, Black Lives Matter Atlanta, The SisterCARE Alliance, The Lotus Legacy Foundation, Dr. Deanine Halliman, M.A.D.E., Spendefy, Dr. Khalil Cumberbatch, Dr. Jewel Crawford, Kareena Cumberbatch, SHINE, Octavia Raheem, Movement Knowledge, Revolutionary Moms Club, Sister Love, Sister Song, 100 Black Women, YBF Publishing LLC, Compassionate Nurses, Georgia State University Office of African American Student Services & Program, Let Us Make Man, and my cultural family the AfriSalsa Cultural Organization-- thank you for your support and for reminding me although I am supported, it is always bigger than me. A special thank you to the

MommyUncensored™ production family for helping me laugh through my introduction to mamahood as a form of emotional self-care. To Ms. Nia Sade Walker, thank you and the YBF Publishing family for assisting with my final push to publish this five year old book writing journey.

To the elders, Dr. Doris Derby, Dr. Marimba Ani, Dr. Mildred McClain, Mama Aminata and Baba Akinyele Umoja, Mama Afiya Madzimoyo and Baba Wekesa Madzimoyo thank you for imparting your wisdom, guidance and expectations on me to continue serving beyond what I ever thought I could accomplish.

To my first baby that came into my life for only a short while, thank you dear Jamari for our short time together. To my son, Zaiire Jasiri Dean Parris, you came into this world a powerful source of inspiration and healing for me. Without you both choosing me to be your mother, I would have never known agape love nor how strong I really am. Zaiire, you share your mama with the community I love, sat on my lap as I finished this book and made everything worth it. I pray through my actions you can be proud to say I am your mother and remember that your gifts are meant to uplift our community and that each self-care choice you make, honors those who fought so you may have the option to do more than just survive. And last but certainly not least, to Derrick Parris, for walking this walk of family with me, no map, no cliff notes, only our desire to build a healthy family unit through love. Thank you for believing in me and sharing two children with me. Thank you for being an excellent father and pouring into our family every day.

I am overwhelmed with gratitude to everyone named and unnamed for supporting and encouraging the writing, publishing, proofreading and sharing of this book, my second scariest birthing experience in life. You all are my Dream Team.

Table of Contents

Appendices

Foreword By: Mawuli Mel Davis

Tell no lies, claim no easy victories. - Amilcar Cabral

The above quote from the brilliant Guinea-Bissauan and Cape Verdean nationalist thinker and political leader, the late Amilcar Cabral, was directed towards revolutionaries engaged in organizing the "masses" in his countryman's struggle against colonialism. Cabral is described as the "greatest leader in the 20th Century" in the Art of Leadership by Oba T'Shaka.

Cabral studied the social structure of his people and he used that information to train organizers who engaged in revolutionary change in his homeland. He instructed these organizers to not lie to the masses, but to instead, disclose the "difficulties, mistakes and failures" to them. These instructions to revolutionaries were given by Cabral in what appears to be his sincere effort to push forward revolutionary theory and practice with integrity and clarity. However, upon closer examination of these fairly simple instructions by Cabral, one is forced to grapple with the practicality of being completely honest with people to whom you are seeking to provide direction and leadership.

The most obvious concern is that by sharing these "mistakes" and "failures" the organizer could lose the confidence of the people. As mothers, fathers, caretakers business owners and activists, we realize the critical role confidence plays in our ability to move forward positively in our families, communities and organizations. The Honorable Marcus Garvey provided his wise instruction on this topic when he declared: "If you haven't confidence in self, you are twice defeated in the race of life. With confidence, you have won even before you have started."

Self Care Matters... A Revolutionary's Approach encourages us to "tell no lies," while simultaneously calling forth a new confidence in who we are and what we can become when we engage in self-care. I am certain some of us who are leaders may still question whether such an approach could result in the loss of confidence by community, and even family members who view us as "servant-leaders." We tend to believe that people must see us as nearly perfect or superhuman for them to continue to believe in us and respect our leadership. Too many of us fail to realize the power in people knowing our failures and frailties, yet witnessing our constant pursuit to be better as we work to raise families, build businesses, sustain organizations or even change the world. Thankfully, in the tradition of Cabral, Anana Harris Parris has developed a Self Care Plan that allows us to share our "difficulties, mistakes and failures," which will allow us to grow and heal together.

The development of the Self Care Plan, Self Care Playbook, and the "Self Care Movement" is born out of the heart and mind of a child born to a revolutionary father and mother. Anana Harris Parris is able to provide insight and reflection for community organizers, parents, service providers and activists because she was raised by her father, Herget Dean Sababu Harris, who valued all these roles while working as a student activist alongside her mother, Kathleen Ann Assata Albert at Southern University during the Civil Rights Movement. I have worked with Anana for more than a decade as a co-laborer in the social justice movement, which seeks to radically change the quality of life and conditions of people who have historically been marginalized and disenfranchised. Our organizing efforts together have ranged from developing campaigns to raise awareness about the Reparations Movement, to organizing a march in Atlanta of over 5,000 protestors after the George Zimmerman verdict.

She is truly the most innovative and creative organizer that I have worked with in my 23 years as an activist. She has continually organized with her heart and head, as she has built strategic alliances and overcome challenges with a compassionate and loving approach. *Self Care Matters... A Revolutionary's Approach* is an extension of the compassion and love that Anana has for her community and those who take care of others.

Self Care Matters... A Revolutionary's Approach is a truly loving approach that challenges the lay person and the "givers" of our world to reexamine their own needs and lives, and for us to "tell no lies" in the process. It is a gentle and workable plan that, when used properly will motivate us to access, address and empower the spiritual, emotional, economic, artistic, physical, educational, and social areas of our lives. We are challenged to overcome our *"addiction to distractions"*, *"push through our self-care blocks"* and *"break our A.F.D. loops"* that keeps us from truly delving deeper into the areas of our lives that need healing.

Anana provides a tool that will help those of us who help people on a daily basis ensure our own self-preservation without guilt. She has opened up her own life experiences to provide examples of how she has had to learn how to take better care of herself through her years as a giving activist, mother, daughter, sister and friend, and shares the consequences of not doing so. If each of us attempts to develop our own Self Care Plan as encouraged in this book, I can only imagine the greater impact on the world we can have when we lead healthier and longer lives. We know that often times the work we have yet to do is the painful and difficult internal work on ourselves.

Those of us who are committed to living our purpose and transforming lives will not "claim easy victories," but will do the hard work of engaging in self-care. For us to experience life at its fullest, we are called to struggle for justice for others and to heal ourselves through self-care. Cabral reminds us that there is no contradiction with our duty as organizers and experiencing joy in our own lives when he says: "nothing of this is incompatible with the joy of living, or with love for life and its amusements, or with confidence in the future and in our work."

Self Care Matters... A Revolutionary's Approach will help us experience the "joy of living" and have "confidence in the future and in our work". Asante Sana (Thank You Very Much) to Anana Harris Parris and to the family and community that has sustained her.

In Struggle, Love, & Victory... Mawuli Mel Davis

Why I Wrote This Book

Your silence will not protect you.-- Audre Lorde

I wrote this book because I realized my desperate need to be honest about the oppressive experience of shame and embarrassment. I wanted to create a program I could personally use to recover and grow from the experiences that made me feel too weak to standup for myself, from being surrounded by people and an environment who were conditioned to benefit from me not speaking up for myself and not taking care of myself. Many well-meaning folks would say things like, *'but you are so good at speaking up in other areas -- what's wrong?'* or *'just do better taking care of yourself next time'* without providing me with a way that was kind, clear and methodical to do so. I wrote this book because I know I am not the only one.

I wrote this book because I wanted to contribute something to help others baby step their way into daily self-care and see that as a revolutionary act.

This book came from a series of harsh challenges in my life, some of which I discuss in here. I wrote this book to free me and you from the invisible villain called emotional slavery. Emotional slavery is when your emotions repeatedly entrap you and prevent you from freely caring for yourself. I wrote this book because you can't see emotional slavery. It lives in the ridicule of others, the unspoken abuses in households and in mass aggressive acts dropped on our chests as a people every day by this machine we call a society, a society that only cultural healing can breathe life into.

I wrote this book because I have moments of extreme courage and extreme fear. I have an ongoing need to recover and heal from each sucker punch life throws at me. Just when I get the hang of healing from an old wound a new wound is inflicted. I just could not figure out how to heal fast enough while still living. I also needed a community of people who care whether or not I take care of myself and who see how clearly critical it is we all talk about the walk of revolutionary self-care together.

I needed help, so I created a program and I am asking you to join me in it. Not because I need the company, but because we need each other to survive and thrive as a community.

I wrote this book because someone told me I wasn't attractive at a moment I didn't feel attractive and I believed them. Someone didn't care if I didn't understand in a classroom so I believed it was too hard to balance life and learning at the same time. Someone treated me as if I wasn't worth speaking to face-to-face regarding an important issue and I believed them. Someone told me I wasn't a good mother because I worked a job and I believed them. Someone told me I was pretty for a dark-skinned girl and I believed them. Someone told me I deserved a big raise but wasn't going to get one, and I believed that was OK. Someone ignored me and I got used to being ignored. Someone expressed pity for me not knowing how to walk in heels as an adult woman and I felt pity for myself. I wrote this book because on many occasions I have had moments of feeling bad about myself, what I didn't know how to accomplish and embarrassment for who could see what was hard for me.

I wrote this book because all of those experiences and many others left me feeling *less than,* quietly imprisoned and secretly enslaved to feeling bad while covering it up... and, I chose to be free and take care of myself anyway. I chose to take a long shower and dress up while saying "I am beautiful and my body is healthy". I chose to find other ways to make additional income because I deserve it. I chose to create the self-care tools I needed to replace negative damaging thoughts with my *niara* Self Care Soap. I requested a face-to-face meeting to share my true thoughts about how a friend hurt me because I was worth it. I asked for guidance from other wiser mothers to help me heal from feeling like I wasn't a good enough mother because mine didn't raise me.

I wrote this book because I had believed what people thought about me mattered more than it should. I rarely spoke up when they treated me unfairly, and I had a hard time sustaining my own self-worth with people I cared about. I believed walking away was the only way when I was really just running from the challenge of speaking up for myself. I stopped running. I stopped leaving until after I found the courage to care enough about myself to respectfully speak up.

I want you to read this book to build courage in you along with those in your family and community to take care of yourself, one self-care act at a time. Read this book and lead by example so you can join me in this journey, because raising your self-worth one self-care step at a time works. Being a self-care revolutionary often takes a village that cares and practices self-care as well. I wrote this book because the answer to your self-betterment is you becoming an aggressive Self Care Revolutionary in every category of your life. The answer and inspiration for you to better *care* for yourself will not lie in the hands of a judge and jury with deconstructive uncompassionate criticism fueling unfair inhumane non-rehabilitating sentencing. The answer is not in the disgusted and passive puns from socialites pointing out how flawed you and those 'like you' are. I wrote this book because the answer is not in doing nothing. The answer to your immediate self-betterment is not in friends randomly practicing their pseudo untrained life coaching or psychologist skills on you one random conversation and venting session at a time. This book was written because downward destructive spirals fueled by unhealthy amounts of sugar, sex, drugs or alcohol to numb your shame and fears of never getting better at taking care of yourself and never feeling empowered will not get you what you need. It will only eventually kill you.

I wrote this book to encourage you to take one revolutionary self-care step at a time acknowledging you are not just a broken soul. You are a soul with some wounds needing healing and care surrounded by others benefiting and profiting from your silence and lack of self-care. I wrote this book because knowing people who may be able to help you spiritually, emotionally, economically, artistically, physically, educationally and socially does not mean you will find the courage to ask them for help. I wrote this book so you can join the revolution to fight for your own self-care as if your sanity, children's future, survival of your business, bank account, community resources, family name and life depended on it. Because no matter what your friends, family, TV commercials, social media 'friends', co-workers, neighbors or romantic partners tell you, all of those critical parts of your life actually *do* depend on you waking up every single day and making the choice to be a Self Care Revolutionary.

What you choose to not care for in your life mirrors what you choose to not see and care for in your community. If you close your eyes to your own spiritual, emotional, economic, artistic, physical, educational or social self-care needs, it will be hard to have the compassion and drive to care about those categories for your community. This book is one essential reference you, your family and your organization should keep close, because showing up to a fight with a sad emoji and a general hope it goes well in every category of care in your life will not help you get freedom. I wrote this book because I was tired of showing up in my own life without a strategy and a plan for how to take better care of myself when no one else is around to know, see and support me through my own true fears, wounds and imprisoning thoughts. I wrote this book so I can share one strategic approach to being free to make impactful self-care choices daily and I want you to come with me. If anything written in this book contributes to helping you feel free to make self-care choices that free you from others causing you harm, a system profiting off your sadness and grief or from your own enslaving thoughts of lack, I truly will feel as if writing every page was worth it. You are loved

and believed in. Come with me and be free one self-care
act   at   a   time.
|#selfcarerevolution |

Chapter 1 – What is Self-Care?

Caring for myself is not self-indulgence, it is self-preservation, and that is an act of political warfare. -- Audre Lorde

When you hear the phrase self-care, what comes to mind? Think about it for a second -- how well do you take care of yourself? How many needs critical to your wellbeing do you attend to and keep track of on a daily basis? Do you even know what those needs are? How many different people do you have to meet with to address all of your various self-care needs? Where do you store the questions, answers and guidance for you spiritual, emotional, economic, artistic, physical, educational and social needs? You may visit a doctor for you physical self-care, a pastor or spiritual guide for your spiritual self-care, a financial advisor or business coach for your economic self-care and maybe a school counselor for your educational self-care. Where are you keeping track of all these self-care goals and critical needs from every category, in your head?

Self-care, as it pertains to the program described in this book, will be defined as any act that addresses needs in regular and critical areas of your life. To enforce critical self-care, one must push through some of the blocks that can stop us from addressing those needs. A crucial question you must begin to ask yourself is -- How can you tell, during the hustle and bustle of a busy day, the difference between a *need* and a *want*?

For the purposes of this book, let's define a *want* as a natural desire-driven feeling and a *need* as something that is crucial to *survival*. For example, you may *want* a piece of cake because you desire it, it tastes delicious and brings you pleasure in the moment. Although, you may *need* a hug because you haven't been touched in a long time, you just went through a significantly difficult battle and the loving safe touch of another human being would warm your soul, giving you more to help you keep going far beyond the sugar rush of a piece of cake. You may *want* to watch your favorite reality show because a laugh would do you good even though you *need* to call your Mortgage Company or landlord to discuss a looming payment deadline. Staying aware of the difference between a *want* and a *need* each day is a crucial self-care skill set that will frame your self-care journey, teach you how to prioritize your day and expedite your freedom.

Being able to tell the difference between a *want* and a *need* is also crucial to developing a good Self Care Plan that battles the blocks to getting what you need in life. Confusing *wants* and *needs* on a regular basis can lead to swift, immediate and quiet *self-care suicide. Self-care suicide* is the gradual quiet ignoring of critical needs until the lack of essential care literally stops your emotional, physical, spiritual, educational, social or economic aspects of your life. This happens every day.

Consistently not checking your bank account or credit, not generating more income and emotionally spending over and over again will eventually kill you financially. Ingesting harmful foods or drink, that harm your body over and over again, ignoring it and not making critical self-care moves to shift the behavior and heal your body will eventually kill you. Spending time on a daily basis with emotionally and physically harmful people that ignore your critical self-care needs will eventually kill you. This daily regular quiet lack of self-care, is self-care suicide. It kills relationships, bank accounts, businesses, community organizations and movements when we ignore what we, our family and our community critically need.

It is no accident that most of us have difficulty deciphering between wants and needs. Every day we are constantly assaulted by the media and advertisements created to focus our attention on what some companies want us to buy. According to research, U.S. businesses spent more than 171 billion dollars in 2013[1] to encourage consumers toward purchases that fuel the economy. That is a large investment of time, money and experts focused solely on guiding and influencing mass decision making. With these strong and well-funded sources working day and night to distract you from your core needs and funding their businesses on your self-care choices, it is no wonder most of us have a hard time determining the difference between a need and a want. You can find yourself personally battling against billions of dollars in market research on spending patterns, think tanks, psychology based research and advertising agency executives who study your every move and dedicated to selling you products or services that frequently have nothing to do with meeting your critical needs.

Think about the old soft drink commercials that often come on before a movie. The large, vivid-colored screen and Dolby surround sound would entice almost every sense to the point to the sight of a fizzy brown liquid being poured over sparkling ice in a frosty glass and peppermint spiraled straw would make you *want* a soft drink. However, if you are truly thirsty, what does your body really *need*? Water, not a fizzy brown drink.

A thirsty body is a sign you are deficient in water, which is essential to so much of our critical bodily functions. It would seem like a simple decision: *I am thirsty. My body needs water. I will drink water.* Unfortunately, when you witness commercial after commercial and hear radio advertisement after radio advertisement, social media ad pop ups and well programmed friends who repeat brand labels and their importance over and over again. Your subconscious is now at the mercy of the advertiser. Techniques like repetition, jingles, and associating celebrities with products are meant to convince you that you not only *need* the product but that you also *want* the emotional experience the product brings for that moment.

Being clear about what you need and staying focused on safely satisfying that need is one of the most revolutionary acts you can perform. In this example, your purchasing choice not only addresses your critical need for water, the act of shifting a regular purchasing pattern (that the company depends on) also strengthens a weak self-care muscle. Translation, you want the drink because of the commercial. You need water because your body is thirsty.

Many of us begin the journey to better self-care confused about the difference between dangerous, indulgent, selfish behavior and true self-care activity. Let's be clear: *self-care is based on addressing a need which also helps heal our core wounds*. The wound that needs healing might be physical, mental, creative, emotional, spiritual or financial. It could be a fresh wound, or it could be an old, long-standing generational wound. Whatever the origin and nature of the wound, it is, nonetheless, a wound that is stopping you from living your best life and it needs caring for. Left unattended, like any wound, it could fester, become infected and contaminate other healthy areas of your life. Acts of self-care allow you to proactively address the real needs that, when addressed, can help heal that wound or deficiency.

Let's look at self-care from a perspective most of us can relate to -- medicine. If you suffer a physical injury, you need specific care for that injury to heal. Would anyone consider you selfish for dressing and treating a wound on your body or for taking medicine when you're sick? No. There is no difference in the need to care for a wounded leg than to care for a wounded bank account or wounded heart after a relationship ends. Any one of these wounds could become critically contaminating to your overall wellbeing, if left unattended. To make your self-care immediate and revolutionary, you must pay attention to and respect the criticality of the wound. Others may not respect the depth of the wound nor be able to relate. You must respect and care for the wound yourself, immediately.

The late healthcare professional and nursing theorist, Dorothea Orem, created the Self Care Deficit Nursing Theory to describe what a patient needs to be considered capable of caring for his or herself. In the theory, Orem defines self-care as the "practice of activities that individuals initiate and perform on their own behalf in maintaining life, health and wellbeing". That definition can be broadened beyond physical wellbeing in the context of this book to include the other aspects that make up a whole life – spiritual, emotional, social, economic, physical, educational, and artistic. So, for our purposes, a self-care action is one that maintains life, health, and well-being in any and all of these categories of care.

As you follow the Self Care Program describe in this book, you will learn how to prioritize real self-care-based actions over other distracting, unproductive behaviors. For example, skipping lunch to spend forty-five minutes on the phone talking about the last episode of your favorite television show on a daily basis instead of having a healthy lunch is probably choosing a distracting want-based behavior over an important need-based, self-care behavior – good nutrition.

Can you distinguish self-care behavior from selfish behavior? Which of the actions described in the scenarios below do you think describe a self-care decision? Ask yourself these questions:

- What is *critical* about what you need in each scenario?
- Are you able to address your critical need and be *respectful of others* at the same time?
- How important are the *relationships* you want to maintain?

Selfish vs. Self-Care

Scenario 1 – Argument Aggravation and Emotional Confusion

You are having an argument with your spouse or significant other. You need to be heard. You also want your spouse to be comfortable and not feel ignored. You decide to respectfully express your opinion and allow your spouse to manage his/hers own emotions.

What is critical about what you need? You need to be *heard.* The only way to work towards making this happen is to speak up. If you need to feel protected and safe more than you need to be heard, then your critical need is to create a safe environment first, then be heard second. *Focus on the most critical need first.* Ask for help and advice from a trusted, caring and qualified person if you are feeling unsafe in any way.

Are you able to address your critical need and be respectful of others at the same time? There is nothing wrong with being angry and showing your anger. Take a breath before speaking your mind. Focus on how you can speak or write the need. If the need is to be heard, then you may need to express your anger and vent in a different scenario so all the focus can be on the other person hearing your words. If the need is to express your anger to a specific person, be sure that mutual respect remains so the scenario doesn't escalate beyond something that you can't control.

Selfish = ignoring basic boundaries of respect when speaking in exchange for 'getting something off your chest.'

Self-care = Investigating what you really need before having a difficult conversation then focusing on creating the best case scenario to respectfully and safely communicate that need.

Scenario 2 – Clean Communication Shows Respect

You cook a big meal and are really tired after eating with the family. You look at the mess in the kitchen and decide to go straight to bed without discussing how the kitchen will be cleaned. You think you shouldn't have to clean up the mess because you cooked.

What is critical about what you need? The need for sleep may feel critical. Or is going to bed without discussing the need for the kitchen to be cleaned the critical need? Does discussing how to get the kitchen clean stop you from meeting your critical need or postpone it? Note: The extra energy it would take to communicate with your family, ask them to help with the kitchen or thank them for assisting with the kitchen would not impede your path to bed.

Are you able to address your critical self-care need and be respectful of others at the same time? If sleep right after cooking and eating is critical, you could address your need before the moment happens and respectfully discuss a clean-up plan with your family, even if the plan involves you waking up early to do it in the morning.

How important is the relationship to the quality of your life? The relationships in our own homes and day to day lives affect us, whether we want them to or not. The extra effort to acknowledge those relationships is not only important but also a part of a critical need. You will want to incorporate good communication with important relationships to help distinguish selfish behavior from self-care behavior. *Spoiler alert*: The more you integrate respect and self-care, the more self-care decisions turn out to be good for you *and* the group. When you look at what you critically need, you can usually begin to better prepare others before you begin adjusting your behavior. Not speaking up about your self-care needs before implementing them is a guaranteed way to make your journey harder. Speaking up is a form of self-care and respecting others by communicating is how you show you care for the people in your life.

Why Self Care is Revolutionary?

You cannot buy the revolution. You cannot make the revolution. You can only be the revolution. It is in your spirit, or it is nowhere. — Ursula K. Le Guin, The Dispossessed

Typically the word *revolution* inspires visions of war, and loud outspoken demands meant to push an obvious evil injustice out of the way while a crowd of people march behind a few or just one caricatured brave leader. In terms of self-care, you could say the war is between the social determinants in your community, your addiction to distraction and your subconscious acts of self-destruction, self-abuse, and self-neglect. The evil injustice is the negative belief and behavioral patterns imbedded in your psyche or mind by those who benefit from you pain. On the other hand, the brave leader and revolutionary is also you. When everything around you is promoting one thing, but you

14

choose to fight for something that shifts you, other people and the environment around you to something completely different and better, you are a revolutionary.

A Self Care Revolutionary knows that *everything* that isn't supporting critical needs must change immediately. A Self Care Revolutionary develops a plan, implements a strategy and places people around them who support and believe in their cause. If that revolutionary's body is completely dehydrated, he or she will not wait a week before drinking water. Rather, he or she will find the water and consume it immediately. A revolution is not about waiting for others to make things easier for you who can't see how critical and immediate your needs are to come around to your way of thinking. A revolution is about pairing up with those who agree with what is critical and the continuous push to maintain a constant flow of resources and support that help expand the movement until there is a new fair and just norm servicing the crucial care needs of everyone in the community.

A revolutionary is an agitator whose arch nemesis is the imaginary comforting feeling of *normalcy* promoted by the status quo i.e. those who determine what is 'cool'. The feeling of being a part of a normal everyday popular act like eating a big delicious breakfast of eggs, pancakes, sausage and orange juice for example makes many feel unified, connected and full. This breakfast can satisfy not only a hunger, but a need for the security of consistency, and bonding with others who also enjoy it. Unfortunately, the illusion of normalcy can accompany acts that can also cause you harm. If you are a borderline diabetic and do not know it, that need to feel normal while craving a big breakfast daily could be slowly pushing you towards permanently harming the organs in your body. Respect the need to feel normal long enough to know exactly how revolutionary your self-care act will need to be. What new normal can you create and who can help support the revolutionary act of self-care you are about to make? Being a self-care revolutionary is just that simple. Make one self-care act at a time while fighting to create a new normal.

Normal is not always good. There can be harm, suppressed suffering and micro-aggressions in *normal* everyday acts. Catching a cab, Uber or booking an Airbnb can be seen as normal except when you're regularly ignored or declined by the drivers or hosts because you're black. Going to work can be seen as *normal* unless you're a woman being paid 40% less than a man for doing the same job. The prevalence and normalization of the daily micro-aggressions many of us experience make each self-care choice to heal from and change the exposure to these aggressions an immediate act of revolution. Normalcy is not always good. Think about how *normal* it is to walk past a homeless person and decide not to speak, let alone make eye contact, or a donation. You may not have any extra money, feel nervous about your safety or you may believe you can't help, and yet should it be *normal* to ignore them, these human beings?

The comfort of normalcy can distract us from what is healthy for us and human about us. We can mistakenly be practicing behaviors that are deconstructing our softness, our compassion and our humanity in exchange for the comfortable consistency of *normalcy*. Constructing a Self Care Plan is revolutionary. It challenges your current comforts and forces you to create a new normal rooted in satisfying your critical spiritual, emotional, artistic, physical, economic, educational and social needs.

Back to the example of homelessness and our *normal* reactions to it. Some of us react towards witnessing homelessness or seeing others in grave need in the same way we react to gut-wrenching challenges in our own lives, challenges that we believe can't be easily solved and scare us. We normalize walking past our challenges with every morning reach for our cell phones in the morning instead of engaging in prayer or a quiet moment. We walk past a sink filled with dirty dishes, a rapidly decreasing bank account many days away from payday – we keep walking. An emotionally abusive relationship with a manager at work – we keep walking.

What makes you a revolutionary, a Self Care Revolutionary, is when you respond to your personal challenges by *acknowledging* them and not walking past them. Mismanaging your money, ignoring regular doctor appointments, remaining in emotionally abusive environments – these are some of the behaviors and wounds many of us have normalized and pseudo-treated by looking for the best products or social media exchanges to distract and soothe our way past them.

A Self Care Revolutionary knows that normalcy contaminated by harm or hurt must change immediately. A complete revolution from seeing these things as *normal* to seeing a new normal as meaning *whole health* in every category of life is what a Self Care Revolutionary fights to make happen.

For a person to believe self-care is revolutionary, she or he has to first see clearly that certain environments and people within those environments encourage and benefit from their own poor self-care choices and the self-care choices of masses of people. For a person to decide to be a Self Care Revolutionary, she or he would have to see clearly that struggling with critical areas in their life without a Self Care Plan doesn't put them in the best long standing position to heal or lead other individuals, families and communities also struggling to improve.

The day you choose to no longer accept what is being shoved down your throat as a contaminated normal working against your basic self-care needs, is the day you become a Self Care Revolutionary.

The Self Care Plan outlined in this book guides you towards creating a new normal rooted in addressing your specific spiritual, emotional, artistic, physical, social, economic and educational needs. Your lifestyle can become a Self Care Revolutionary lifestyle, foiling the plans of those who profit when you are in pain, who flourish when you are afraid to do something different and who secure the financial and social standings of their own future generations on the backs of your challenged self-care choices. You foil those plans for them to profit off of your pain when your financial, physical, emotional, spiritual, educational and social self-care habits are not only strengthened but also passed on to your children.

You do not have to be perfect, you only need to care and have a plan.

To maintain a regular feeling of freedom while working your Self Care Plan, remember you are a Self CARE Revolutionary not a Self PERFECTION Revolutionary. The key word is care. You are actively caring about your needs. | #participationnotperfection | There are multiple areas of your life you want to improve on so stressing yourself out about being perfect will end this journey to freedom before it truly can take shape and begin. Remember this mantra, 'participation not perfection. Think about it: when you try to find the time and the motivation to do better in your life by changing your self-care habits regarding your environment, your friends and your financial resources, each effort to do so can feel like trying to stop a million leaks in boat:

You want to eat better foods but you will need more money because healthy food is more expensive -- *leak*.

Your workplace is stressing you out and takes up so much time you don't have the time you need to rest, recover from your day AND look for another job -- *leak*.

The relationship with your significant other has been spiritually and emotionally taxing for years yet you stay for the financial security blanket -- *leak*.

You have dreams of starting a business yet your social circle spends the majority of their extra time complaining about life and emotionally spending -- *leak*.

When you look in the mirror, you always see something you want to change about your body and your moments of depression hijack every opportunity for you to push for working out while loving on the body you have -- *leak*.

In order to stop your entire *life ship* from sinking, or beating up on yourself every day to merely stop leaks, you will need to have a Self Care Revolutionary mindset and a Self Care Plan. Stopping every leak will always feel impossible when you have no plan and no strategy. Pleasing friends and family cannot be the priority of a revolutionary nor a part of your plan ... only respecting them. Realizing your life purpose and how to be healthy enough to fulfill it is your priority. Your life's purpose will only show itself as a need not a want.

Your life's purpose will only show itself as a need not a want.

For example, if you *need* to help children, if you *need* to be a wonderful parent or if you need to break a generational behavior pattern, that is a part of your purpose and must be included in your spiritual and emotional Self Care Plan category. Allowing unhealthy acts or abusive environments to control your life and distract your attention away from your purpose and critical self-care needs is not the direction of a Self Care Revolutionary – fulfilling your life purpose is an act of self-care and the direction of a Self Care Revolutionary.

Revolutionaries are usually only seen as cool or *on fleek* when what they do is public and actually works immediately to help others (and that may not be realized until long after their death). Typically, in the beginning, nobody likes a revolutionary because it can be scary supporting someone who is choosing to speak out about normalized injustices that are widely accepted. For that reason, not many revolutionaries start out with support for their passion and desire for change. There is no popular revolutionary 101 course, nor a business model outlined to guide a new revolutionary to make perfect decisions every time. However, when it works, the revolutionary's hard work and faith to persevere benefits more than just him or her and the movement proceeds.

Once you begin adopting a Self Care Revolutionary mindset and implementing a Self Care Plan, the fear of failing begins to shrink. You will begin addressing critical needs that have been creating the leaks in the boat, the same leaks that cause a level of anxiety preventing you from making clear decisions.

Unaddressed critical *financial* needs can cause anxiety whether you try to walk past them or not. Unaddressed critical *emotional* needs can cause a stress and worry that force impulse decision making or breakdown your immune system. Unaddressed critical *social* needs can limit your ability to accept and be exposed to more help and resources.

It takes courage to face your critical needs. However, over time, the reduction of that anxiety, worry, lack of resources and support builds you up in ways you never knew were possible. Leaks begin to be sealed up one at a time then two at a time and you have more control over the direction of that once-sinking boat.

A little courage focused on addressing a self-care need causes a self-care snowball effect that helps to shrink your fear of failing while beginning seeing more options opening up in your life. Working the Self Care Plan (with no arbitrary deadlines or judgements) allows you to quiet your worst critic -- you. It is hard to embarrass Self Care Revolutionaries because they know they are working a Self Care Plan not a Self *Perfection* Plan. There is nothing embarrassing about being able to say you are actively working a plan.

Many people are afraid to be a revolutionary because they feel as if they should have all the answers immediately. But that's not true. Revolutionaries are clear about what the need is and meeting that need is always more important than impressing someone. When a need is critical and you are able to focus on it, it colors your entire day. Anyone you encounter who doesn't respect the critical nature of your need, will not influence your daily path. This is why it is hard to embarrass a revolutionary: a Self Care Revolutionary is too focused on and clear about meeting a need to be embarrassed.

With a Self Care Plan, you are telling yourself, *"I'm not playing around anymore."* Temporary comfort will still win a lot of the time over the hard work of change. However, it won't win over success: the success of the feeling of freedom when you have repaired and improved your credit score or losing the jittery shaky addictive feeling sugar brings when you haven't had it in a while, for example. Once you begin to plug up those financial leaks one at a time and go to sleep at night feeling a new sense of security that a bill will be paid, being a Self Care Revolutionary will feel better than trying to hide from fear and pain through unhealthy and scary poor self-care behavior. It feels better to have a Self Care Plan that works on meeting your needs.

We want everything to be fixed right away, and being a revolutionary requires a certain kind of focus and faith in knowing that the steps involved in getting to that better credit score, healthier body, better work environment or higher education requires a plan and support that *you* have the ability to create for yourself even in the face of unbelievable obstacles. Without a good Self Care Plan, the slow leaks you are currently ignoring will eventually cause your life to capsize. For example, cleverly covering up the fact that you are living paycheck to paycheck will catch up to you. Pretending like the pain in your stomach you have been feeling over the last several weeks will disappear by itself will catch up to you.

Every revolutionary is about freedom. True freedom can be had one self-care choice at a time. Denying yourself the things you need to survive and thrive is you creating your own personal form of slavery to contaminated normalcy and fear. Being able to live your purpose is freedom. Through improving and increasing your self-care choices, you can better secure the impact of your purpose and reach more people. Move toward freedom one self-care baby step at a time and enjoy a new revolutionary walk.

You are a Self Care Revolutionary when the people and environments in life don't support your self-care needs *but* you choose to face them, create a Self Care Plan and take care of yourself anyway. |#selfcarerevolutionary|

Why Self Care Matters

When a person is able to go through life without ever experiencing the feeling of being at the mercy of someone or a circumstance, you might consider that person extremely fortunate. If you know what it feels like to be at the mercy of a person or situation that has control over your time, your paycheck, when you eat, sleep or pray, then you know why self-care is important.

Self-care is the act of accessing what thoughts, environment, behaviors and immediate resources can help you move one step closer to getting what you need. The emptiness you feel in your gut when you can't satisfy a basic need like hunger, medical care or lack of physical touch is the core reason self-care is important. It hurts to feel like you cannot meet a core need you have. The act of self-care matters because to stay in hurt is slavery, prison and death. Self-care is not just your bare minimum survival needs, like breathing, it is also your need to thrive and sustain growth in life.

Self-care strips every situation down to one question: *what do I need?* When I do workshops or speaking engagements, this very question stumps half the audience immediately especially when I ask it for every category of care. We will always be at the mercy of another a person or situation until we take the first step towards learning how to answer that question quickly for ourselves spiritually, emotionally, economically, artistically, physically, educationally and socially.

The importance of self-care is painfully obvious when one dysfunctional area of our lives begins contaminating another. This contamination can taint the joy we experience as we slowly get stuck in a pattern of *at the mercy* behavior and thoughts: *I am at the mercy of my job. I am at the mercy of my spouse. I am at the mercy of my past.* Repeating *at the mercy* behavior slowly erases the desire to take care of ourselves because our spirit and soul feel crushed and crumbled when we feel at the mercy of others. Creating a Self Care Plan gives us something to focus on and control by aiming our energy and focus towards bettering our lives through the use of a plan.

Some of us learned to respond to situations with *at the mercy* behavior and thoughts without actually being at the mercy of anything! Our parents or other adults may have passed on this behavioral response without us even knowing it. It's something like flinching at punch that was never thrown. For instance, thinking you aren't good enough to stand next to or work with a particular person is an *at the mercy of* feeling that may have been taught. Did someone teach you that you weren't good enough? Before introducing yourself, maybe you make assumptions about what other people think about you. As a result, you flinch prematurely and say something to diminish any positive impression of you they may be forming. Putting yourself down before someone else can is a wonderful example of feeling at the mercy of a person or environment when the person or environment hasn't provided a reason for you to feel that way. Breaking the cycle of feeling at the mercy of a person or situation takes baby steps and a Self Care Revolutionary mindset.

None but ourselves can free our mind. --Bob Marley, Redemption Song

Chapter 2: Categories of Care

Allowing your desire for someone else to take care of you to repeatedly trump your desire to take care of yourself, is a guaranteed way to remain at the mercy of and emotionally enslaved by others.
— Anana Harris Parris

Before we go any further, let's take a look at the categories of care that make up the Self Care Plan. Feel free to visit SelfCareAgency.com to download your own personal Self Care Check-In Form. The categories were specifically chosen to encompass the various primary areas of a life. There are multiple ways we can slice and label our lives. For the purpose of this program, the following categories were chosen: Spiritual/Emotional, Economic, Artistic, Physical, Educational, and Social -- S.E.A.P.E.S.

Self Care Revolutionary Assignment: List what you critically need just in this very moment for each category of care listed below.

Spiritual/Emotional

Joy. Sorrow. Anger. Fear. Love. Hope. Faith.

This category references all areas and goals pertaining to your emotional and spiritual wellbeing, the areas that inspire you with hope and faith beyond the things you can see or touch. Emotions without a spiritual reference leave you at the mercy of anybody who can cause an emotional response in you. It leaves your behavior and dreams at the mercy of whatever controls your emotional reactions. Living with raw emotions one day to the next can lead you away from your dreams. Connecting your spiritual needs to your emotional ones is a way to take a leadership role in your own life. Your spirit is what moves you when nothing else can. It can be heightened and nurtured and encouraged to make you feel free, accepted or loved. Your spirit can also make you feel broken, beaten, unwelcomed and imprisoned when it is exposed to harm and challenges in life. Spiritual/Emotional self-care acts are critical to create daily in your life for you to:

- Acknowledge what you need

- Recognize your purpose
- Understand your purpose
- Sustain the path of your purpose
- Stay connected to others who compliment your purpose and,
- Recognize the healthy environments and relationships in which your spirit can heal and flourish.

Emotional honesty and transparency is respected as authentic, yet emotions with active faith and hope engaged can ease your journey through life. The thoughts in your mind and your mental health require a healthy spiritual and emotional foundation to function properly. Thoughts can get crowded around emotional pain and a lack of hope, making it almost impossible to logically think your way out of every situation. Self-care baby steps and actions of a spiritual and emotional nature should always stem from honesty. Caring for yourself spiritually and emotionally should be a gentle and kind experience.

Spiritual/Emotional Need Examples:

- Praying after a tough moment
- Listening to a favorite song loudly
- Receiving a kind word or guidance from someone that helps you learn how to best determine or address your spiritual and emotional self-care needs
- Finding a space in which to be honest and in which to heal

Economic

Economics is a term that tends to be referenced solely to address finances however, for the purpose of this Self Care Program, *economics* holistically defines the management of your time, money and energy. Acknowledging the management of your time, money and energy is a healthy start to improving how you manage your life.

Economic Need Examples:

- Having someone to advise you how to best prioritize and face your economic self-care needs

- Keeping a calendar of obligations (financial, time, social commitments)
- Knowing what's in your bank account
- Balancing how you spend your time in the course of a day
- Knowing the difference in friends who take your energy without giving good energy and those who give and receive good energy

Artistic

Artistic self-care is an act that fuels creative growth, healing, healthy expression and change. For critical self-care goals, artistic self-care is a wonderful way to affordably surround yourself with a healing emotional and spiritual experience. Creating or sharing artistic expression is truly a divine gift to yourself and others. Whether it is culinary arts, painting, dance, poetry, singing, drawing, designing clothes, styling hair or producing film, art and creativity stimulate ideas and help us express what we can't always verbalize. Baby steps in this category should expose you to experiencing and/or creating art for the purpose of feeding all your other self-care needs. Never feel pressured to participate beyond your comfort level. Watching and enjoying without talking is one of the many gifts artistic self-care can bring.

Artistic Need Examples:

- Be around artistically expressive people
- Seeing something beautiful and experiencing it in a way you never have before
- Sing out loud
- Draw or color without judgement

Physical

Your body houses more than food, muscles and bones. Your body also houses the emotional pain and worry you feel on a day-to-day basis. Working out, dancing, stretching, walking or any form of healthy movement is not just about working the muscles and organs in your body, it is also about proactively addressing the connection of how you feel emotionally to how you feel physically. Your physical health is important not just because your body gets you from point A to point B. Your physical health also matters because it's connected to what helps you reach your dreams and fulfill your purpose. Baby steps in this area should be towards building strength and stamina, improving your quality of life, and relieving the stress and worry generated while working towards accomplishing your dreams.

Physical Need Examples:

- Have fun while you move your body
- Learn how to heal an ailment or injury
- Take a dance lesson
- Find someone to advise and help you learn how to prioritize your physical self-care needs

Educational

Educational self-care is about finding what you want to learn and using that knowledge to help you achieve your purpose in life. Gifts of knowledge on how to reach your dreams and goals in life are all around you. Determining what you want to accomplish in life helps to determine what you need to learn. Being open to learning can help you move along the journey to reaching your dreams. Baby steps in this area directly relate to learning through text, people, programs, institutions and life lessons on how to reach your dreams.

Educational Need Examples:

- Knowing your educational options
- Having access to a way to pay for educational needs
- Having someone to advise you who is non-critical and helps you learn how to best determine or address your educational self-care needs
- Learning ways to learn with less struggle and/or less shame

Social

Social self-care focuses on interacting with others to assist us as we work to reach our dreams and fulfill our purpose. Whether your socializing involves volunteering to help those less fortunate, networking to promote your dreams and initiatives or spending time with those who share your passion for a topic, social self-care is a critical category. It not only helps you reach your goals, it also offers the gift of giving when you share your time with others. Many times just your presence in a healthy state of mind brings joy to others.

By communing with others, we are invited to be present and share. We are invited to find the courage to believe in what we are saying and sharing by doing just that -- sharing. Face-to-face communications will remain some of the most impactful experiences in your life. As society offers the option to decrease the prevalence of face-to-face socializing, we must be all the more proactive about this self-care category. Baby steps in this category stem from the needs of our dreams and the gift of sharing our presence with others.

Social Need Examples:

- Being in environments that compliment my personal, professional or entrepreneurial goals
- Countering a tough day or week with people and environments that allow you to relax and be yourself
- Having someone advise you who helps you learn how to best determine or address your social self-care needs

- Being around positive people without feeling pressured

Areas Where You Can Express Self Care

As you learn more about the details of a Self Care Plan, you will see the various areas in life in which such a plan can be implemented and maintained.

Personal & Family Life

Self-care within your family is not only your responsibility, but your CONTRIBUTION to the stability of the familial support unit. You are only able to do your part if you are sound physically, spiritually, and emotionally. It's an ongoing commitment, and one of the greatest ways you can show your love. -- Melissa Fox, Chief Operating Officer, Robin's Nest, Mother & Wife

In our personal and family lives, we attempt to intertwine self-care activities with busy schedules and microwave experiences. Rarely do we have a dedicated place to talk about how we take care of ourselves holistically. In our personal life, we hold memories of what helps us through difficult times or if we are lucky, our friends remind us how strong we are and have been. As a survival strategy, some of us join institutions, organizations or even business that help us remember how to replenish ourselves. These beautiful friends and institutions carry us through tough times and dark days. However, what happens when they aren't around or fall short of our expectations? This is why we maintain an active Self Care Plan. We are responsible for our own care.

Sometimes, without labeling it, without being formerly taught about it or without writing it down as a structured plan, we create personal systems of care. For instance, a friend may mention how much she loves her dentist, which could trigger a thought about the last time you had a cleaning and, as a result, you make an appointment. Someone else may mention that they're on a budget and can't afford to join you for dinner. This might trigger the idea that you should save your own money and cook a meal instead. By default, and without a formal plan, we make simple and impactful self-care decisions every day. What if in our personal and family lives, we all proactively support the discussion, encouragement and planning of self-care in our lives with each other?

The Missing Self Care Manual

If I knew then what I know now, my life would still have difficulties but at least I would feel better about myself along the way -- Anonymous

There are many lessons we are taught in life as a child. Ideally, one of the lessons, behaviors and habits we learn is how to take care of ourselves. In a 2013 report of the Federal Interagency Forum on Child and Family Statistics stated the following:

"Good emotional and behavioral health is an integral part of healthy development and enhances a child's sense of well-being, supports rewarding social relationships with family and peers, and facilitates achievement of full academic potential. Children with emotional or behavioral difficulties may have problems managing their emotions, focusing on tasks, and/or controlling their behavior. These difficulties, which may persist throughout a child's development, can lead to lifelong problems." -- Source: *America's Children: Key National Indicators of Well-Being*

With that said, who taught us this integral part of healthy development? What about those who aren't taught how to care for themselves. Someone once said our youth is about learning and our adult life is about unlearning all that doesn't work for us. What if a key component was never taught? For instance, how we are taught to understand and manage ourselves spiritually, emotionally, artistically, physically, educationally, economically and socially can be a critical determining factor for attaining peace, success and growth in our lives. Yet, many of us are so preoccupied with managing the day-to-day, there is rarely any time to think about what key lessons our childhoods were missing. Where is this missing manual, this missing self-care manual we all need to help guide us through our overall self-care?

Anana's Missing Manual

43

In my twenties, in therapy, I remember spending an inordinate amount of time examining a past trauma I experienced as a child while new life challenges were happening simultaneously. It became overwhelming, so I stopped facing the trauma and ignored my current challenges by using dance, an occasional visit to church, good food and good company. But clearly that wasn't enough. The reality of my twenties was, I was flailing from one moment to the next, praying the basic self-care actions I learned growing up and the few safe things I thought helped me feel better would sustain me. I thought what I was doing was healthy enough because not all of my self-care actions were destructive. I would say "at least I'm not doing this or at least I'm not doing that."

Dancing was healthy for me physically, emotionally and socially. Every time I performed with my first dance company, Balafon West African Dance Ensemble, it helped me grow more confident in life. As a result of rigorous rehearsals, I had a healthy body and a network of support based on something I felt connected to, West African dance. I used to work a full eight hours in downtown Washington, D.C., then head to a one-hour West African dance class taught by the artistic director of Balafon, Kadiatou Conte. After the dance class, I would participate in a two-hour rehearsal, then finally head to the Republic Gardens, a club that had a salsa night hosted by an Afro-Latino salsa crew called Moro back then, to round out my full day. I danced, danced and danced some more. I was learning both West African dance and Salsa simultaneously, which kept me physically fit and socially connected. I thought I was doing enough to manage the stressors in my life because I was doing all of this while working full time.

What wasn't happening was a balance of attention to my other self-care categories. I neglected, closed my eyes to and completely ignored critical needs in other categories with no plan on how to address them. I only had physical, artistic, social and some emotional care handled, but spiritual, economic and educational self-care took a back seat regularly. I had no wise elders or experienced caring people I asked for help from in those areas. By only addressing my self-care in certain areas, I left myself unprepared and unprotected in the other categories of care. I was not proactive about addressing what I really needed in those missing areas, and it took a toll. For me to really be holistically progressing in life, I needed to pay attention to all of my self-care categories one baby step at a time. Don't get me wrong, there were many ways I could have coped that were unhealthy. I chose not to drink because, growing up, I'd seen enough people who had abused alcohol. I blocked out past trauma and current fears using dance, thinking that would be enough. Blocking out fears is not healing them. There was no balance, no preparation, no strategy nor plan for better caring for myself or my future. My self-care manual was missing not just because I had not yet created one, but because no one is given a self-care manual in life. Not having a Self Care Manual, Plan and Strategy was and is... normal. What is beautiful is you can now write one for yourself.

Needing a Plan

At this time in my life, I had not yet acknowledged nor respected the state of my economic challenges, lack of educational care options and spiritual emotional challenges. I didn't yet realize that it was essential to manage my time, money and energy, to expand my knowledgebase, heal spiritually and emotionally from past traumas while surrounding myself with a spiritual support system. I was taking care of myself only in the ways I had the least amount of fear. I had a supportive father, loving friends, and mother and siblings encouraging my growth. However, I was missing a manual with the instructions that I needed to face those fears and keep moving forward.

As a result, in my twenties in those missing categories of care, I began a slow but inevitable move towards self-care suicide. Self-care suicide is when we allow ourselves to consistently ignore critical areas of care in our life long enough for those ignored categories of care to completely shut down our life. For example, you can be as healthy as your body can possibly be, but if you mismanage your finances long enough, you won't be able to afford what it takes to maintain your good health or recover from a physical trauma. If you are socially in tune and comfortable in public settings but never built up a spiritual support system, an emotional or physical trauma could drive you to isolate yourself from that which feeds your spirit.

How do you build a house with no tools or an instructional manual? There are individuals who were raised by parents or grandparents who provided lessons for every category of care. There are others who were left to fend for themselves in terms of self-care lessons and guidance. 'A financial tip here and a shaving lesson there' isn't enough to know how to reach your goals and dreams in life for every category. You need a plan. Having a plan is about being prepared. Creating a Self Care Plan is a form of protection for what you can't see coming.

> *"Self-care strategies for self-defense requires discipline in adopting an evolving skill set built upon the foundations of education, persistent training, and spirited competition. Women in abusive relationships should understand the laws governing their rights to self-defense. This includes but is not limited to understanding the concealed weapon statutes, use of force continuum, and the importance of temporary protective orders. Those who don't realize self-defense is a form of*

self-care continue to be victimized
physically, mentally, and emotionally.
Extreme cases of this abuse is passed
down from one generation to the next.
Those who don't see self-defense as a
form of self-care often become victims.
They panic and/or freeze in a time of
crisis. Education, persistent training,
and spirited competition negates this
phenomena and prepares women
mentally and physically for self-
defense." -- Rashid McCall, President,
Arms In Motion (A.I.M.)

Self Care in Your Work Life

Whether you are a stay-at-home mom, entrepreneur, actively looking for a job, a student or business executive, work-life balance is preached as essential to a healthy lifestyle. Because you are one person, an issue at home affects work life and an issue at work affects the home life. One of the few facts that are consistent between work and home is that your critical needs remain the same no matter where you are. Your personal needs while working will always exist. Self-care in the workplace incorporates the importance of being aware of and satisfying what you need while performing well on the job. Who you choose to bond with, disagree with and seek advice from at work make the time you spend at work a personal experience. Self-care in the workplace takes the same strategy as implementing a Self Care Plan at home -- know what you need, plan to take steps to meet your needs and check in with knowledgeable people along the way.

What often makes your work life feel more complicated and stressful is the looming air of the possible financial repercussions for not doing well or upsetting the wrong person. In the punitive-based non-self-care supportive atmosphere of most businesses, employees tend to make decisions based on fear rather than self-care. When you make decisions at work based on fear, your belief in your ability to create new ways to succeed within or without that company diminishes. To take good care of yourself in your work life and explore every opportunity to fight fear-based decision making, you can implement a Self Care Plan that anchors your time at work with basic practices that reduce stress and promotes preparedness rather than a feeling of entrapment. When you begin to set self-care goals that incorporate regular practices aiding in doing excellent work, continue to help you grow financially and in your career, you will see that that is true freedom. Begin your Self Care Plan today.

Community Organizations and Self Care

As this self-care movement gains momentum, use the principles and activities in this book to strengthen the bonds of the supporters, leaders, staff and founders of your organization. Read through each section and take notes or mark areas you would like to use as opportunities for discussion and empowerment for yourself and your staff. For community organizations riddled with more needs than resources, facing the pressure to support a traumatized community on a regular basis and a staff constantly bombarded with the potential of suffering aggressive compassion fatigue, utilizing this book is critical. My first exposure to the term 'compassion fatigue' was from a gifted and compassionate behavioral psychologist, Dr. Brian McGregor.

"Compassion Fatigue is a state experienced by those helping people or animals in distress; it is an extreme state of tension and preoccupation with the suffering of those being helped to the degree that it can create a secondary traumatic stress for the helper." Dr. Charles Figley

Dr. McGregor is a contributing author to a book titled, "The Social Determinants of Mental Health" which outlines the clear barriers in communities that exist around health services that lead to determining what actual health support is made possible for a particular community. To be a public and social service provider, a community resource service provider or provide regular services to the traumatized you will be affected. You are human. Without a strategic Self Care Plan for yourself, compassion fatigue will set in, fester and numb the impact of the services you and your staff and organization is missioned to offer. Not only will the quality of the services become diminished, neglect and lack of care will contaminate the very service you offer further compounding the damage to the spirit of the person seeking help. Teachers, doctors, nurses, lawyers, counselors, pastors and human resource managers all fall into the big category of those potentially subjected to trauma on a regular basis that need a Self Care Plan.

There is no right or wrong way to use this book. It is a reference tool for you or can be used to instigate a group discussion around self-care. Empowering yourself and your team with a Self Care Plan and in-house Self Care Support Group based on Self Care Plan check-ins also empowers the organization. Knowing and addressing your own needs as a leader helps you better understand how to prioritize the core needs of your organization. Your team will understand that you care not only about your organization growing but also about the growth and health of those who are helping your organization to grow. There are some community-based organizations struggling for funding to keep their doors open while the staff of organization is also struggling in life.

There are some community-based organizations struggling for funding to keep

their doors open while the staff of organization is also struggling in life.

Find a way to plug up one leak at a time inside your organization and for yourself. Many community organizations loose valuable information, expertise and support when their members cover up their critical self-care needs until they burn out. Self-care needs mirrors organizational care needs. Imbalances in addressing all your self-care category needs mirror imbalances in ignoring what you do not like to manage with in your organization. Mirror the steps of a Self Care Plan in your organization and you will be a revolutionary with longevity.

A common storyline, unfortunately, is when leaders of community-based organizations become overwhelmed then encourage, by example, poor self-care habits in their staff. Skipping meals, anger-filled venting based meetings, and uninformed decision making are all poor organizational care habits that stem from the poor self-care behaviors of leaders in a struggling organization. The norm becomes mental, emotional and physical burn out and high turnover for critical community organizations servicing a community that is also mentally, emotionally and physically burned out.

Let's stop this cycle and find the courage to better care for ourselves, our staffs and our communities by adopting the self-care planning strategies in this book within our organizations. This book is a tool, like any other. It works best when it is actually used regularly and introduced by an inspirational leader. Leaders and supporters, begin to care enough for yourself to lead by example while inspiring others to do the same. The same focus that is given to writing a grant or drafting a business plan for your organization can also fuel the development of an organizational or personal Self Care Plan.

Self Care Revolutionary Organization Assignment:

Create or offer to host a voluntary monthly Self Care Support Group for other leaders, your staff and your targeted community. Contact the Self Care Agency and the SisterCARE Alliance to schedule your online or in person training.

Creating Self-Care Habits in a Community

Many factors and influences can derail or discourage an individual's attempt to proactively move towards better self-care. Historically in many societies, negative reinforcement through criticism, blame and punishment has been the primary method of motivation to correct unproductive or wrong behavior. This method of attempting to instigate movement or growth has permeated into school systems, the workplace, community organizations and, of course, in the judicial system. Negative reinforcement to get things done may arguably have a place in some instances. However, the greater issue to be aware of is how present negative reinforcement is used in daily behaviors, policies and laws within our society. Do better or I will punish you. Do better or I'll dock your pay. Do better or you will have to drop a letter grade on your final exam. Punishment as encouragement is normal in our society.

If an individual chooses self-care while being surrounded by an environment of criticism and punishment, that individual will need more than a pat on the back to do better in life. Living in an environment so saturated with the fear of messing up creates lifestyles and decisions based more on fear than self-care. The school systems, workplace and courtrooms primarily are in accordance with streamlining behavior correction towards a punishment-based outcome. This fear-based strategy takes the power of correction, and more importantly the interest in prevention, out of the hands of the individual. Why should a child choose to prevent its own bad behavior when he or she would do better by learning instead to avoid punishment for the behavior? This choice is made every day by children in communities fueled by a fear of punishment rather than by inspiration to care for themselves.

From an institutional perspective, once an error in behavior has occurred, addressing the individual's need to learn how to better care for themselves is rarely the priority. The new priority becomes how the institution or society's needs can be addressed. Society's needs are constantly being prioritized over assisting the individual in meeting their own personal needs. Ideally, both can be achieved.

Every day, we struggle to meet individual needs, community needs and institutional needs. For those communities missing the tools, resources and support that promote self-care as a priority, individuals become dependent on institutions. Self-care education can be a revolutionary act for children and adults, empowering them with practical day-to-day activities. Acknowledging and working to address self-care needs every day spiritually, emotionally, economically, artistically, physically, educationally and socially leads to the betterment of individuals and a community. We have to begin respecting the importance of being gentle, kind and caring with ourselves, our children and our community.

Why is Focusing on Self-Care so Hard?

There can be many factors that can distract you from addressing a need. Let's consider a primal need like love. When love is missing in someone's life, any immediate replacement other than love is like empty calories -- preoccupying the mind but not feeding the need. You wake up still needing love. Tricking the mind into believing that what it needs can be replaced by a general want is the enemy of progress in life. Implementing a Self Care Plan is a proactive move towards assessing and addressing needs. Unfortunately, this is not so easy while being bombarded with messages that are based on feeding temporary, often artificially-manufactured wants.

It is not a person's weakness and character defaults that solely contribute to the difficulty of focusing on genuine self-care needs. Television, mobile phones, monitors in cabs, bars, coffee shops and airports are all laced with the *want* drug. This *want* drug is being administered to you, your friends and family members. Once a person spends their day overly stimulated by gadgets and communication tools, they return home, systematically diverted from what they need. Their mind is now saturated with the idea that what it *wants* is as important as what it *needs*. As each fashion trend and political climate comes and goes, we become more and more exposed to the *want* drug. The online data analysis website *eMarketer* reports in an article titled *US Total Media Ad Spend Inches Up, Pushed by Digital* that US advertisers spent $171.01 billion on paid media in 2013. Entire business models are based on teasing us with the idea of satisfying what we *want,* thereby distracting us from what we need.

For example, let's look at social media. If you have a need to feel connected in a healthy way, social media marketing efforts will have you believe that the first place to begin your search for ways to satisfy that need is to log onto a website and engage in temporary electronic interaction. You need human connection but you settle for computerized attention.

However, the basic need to connect in a healthy way doesn't go away when you log off of social media. Social media is a tool you can use to help meet some of the goals you outline in your Self Care Plan. For example, Salsa dancing is a wonderful way to make human connections and social media is a great way to find a class. Without a Self Care Plan to compliment the use of social media as a tool, you and your subconscious are at the mercy of that $171.01 billion dollars.

If we don't teach newer generations effective methods to address our own needs, the simple pleasures and benefits of satisfying our own needs by our own doing could eventually fade away.

Self Care for Men

Self-care is exceedingly important for men, as the life expectancy of males is significantly shorter than that of their female counterparts. This is primarily due to the fact that many men spend so much time and energy working to provide for their families that it takes a mental, physical and emotional toll that literally shaves years off their lifespans. Men need to consider the fact that if they took better care of themselves, they could provide for their families longer!" -- Allen Germain, Director of the Proyecto Barrio Dance Company and Owner of Rhythmz and Motion Dance Studio

Oftentimes men catch a raw deal. There are assumptions made by many about what a man feels or doesn't feel. When it comes to self-care, it is impossible to address how a man cares for himself without addressing the emotional and social attacks he undergoes each day forcing him to guard those very feelings. Challenges from childhood to adulthood aggravate the attacks men face every day like the social conditioning of suppressing emotions or the constant aggressive and subtle strikes of racism towards men of color. To be bombarded daily with hyper-aggressive racist attacks, assumptions of having no feeling and a social atmosphere created such that others should fear them, black men in particular around the globe specifically have an uphill battle when it comes to self-care. They must first acknowledge a need. This need is typically a sore spot that is exposed during the day, however the majority of a man's day may be spent protecting himself and ignoring his sore spots; his needs.

The key to defeating the challenges around self-care facing black men head on is black men must do two things at once. The self-care revolutionary black man must ward off the enemy with one hand and treat their wounds with the other. Mixed in with each attack during a full day are red flags showing signs of critical issues in your life. A financial red flag may be raised when you are invited to a networking event that comes with a fee. An educational red flag may be raised when you are asked to take on a new project that you need more information on to complete. If the majority of a man's energy is focused on protecting himself from hidden or overt attacks, it is exceptionally hard to notice and address those red flags at the same time. Self-care is about addressing your needs in every category of your life. As a man is built up strong and thick skinned by his family and/or society, that thick skin creates a tunnel of protection making it hard to see these blaring red flags. Keep this method of self-care so you can continue to protect yourself. Become a self-care revolutionary and recognize the red flags that are raised while you are protecting yourself throughout the day.

The tunnel hides feelings, ideas and plans from those who may try to derail or discourage a man. The tunnel walls are thick with the memories of the man or women that caught you slipping. You opened up and were hurt. It could be a family member or a romantic partner. It could be a co-worker or a teacher. Whoever destroyed that trust mixed in with a tiny bit of ego was the perfect cement mixture for your tunnel. I only offer in this self-care program this perspective. If you wake up in the morning and go to sleep at night the same man, you are stuck in a tunnel loop.

If you wake up in the morning and go to sleep at night the same man, you are stuck in a tunnel loop.

A tunnel loop is a dark place that blocks your vision from seeing red flags on your right and left. These red flags can be thrown up by anyone from family and friends to complete strangers. These critical red flag issues must be attended to or your life will buckle. The tunnel only provides you comfort because in there, you have protected yourself from harm. However, your tunnel is so thick, you have not cared for yourself. Only protecting yourself is the life of a survivor. Taking care of yourself is the life of someone who thrives. To thrive you must take a self-care step every day in one category.

You can keep your tunnel of protection, just make it see through. Pay attention throughout your day to the red flags. Make your tunnel of protection transparent. Then, when you get home at the end of the day, take notes on what steps you need to take to accomplish your goal and continue working your Self Care Plan. This is being more than just a survivor. Team up with others who are tired of just surviving and support each other. You are needed as your strongest self in our homes and communities. Men are sorely need in our families.

In writing this book, I spent some time requesting feedback from men about self-care. In theory, the approach shouldn't be different. In reality, men and women continue to be perceived and socialized differently. This is why a separate section is needed. The common link I found when discussing self-care with men and women is the distance between knowing what we need and doing what we need to do to take care of ourselves. The importance of having a game plan in life for men tends to include key factors like, financial stability, respect, trust and authentic brotherhood by any means necessary. In all of those areas, holistic self-care tends to play second fiddle.

*...According to the Centers for
Disease Control and Prevention latest
statistics. We are so unsafe, in fact, that
unintentional injuries- those that occur
without the intent to harm oneself (fires,
car crashes, falling, etc.) -- are men's #3
cause of death after heart disease and
cancer...[men] seem to be oblivious to
the daily dangers that we face. --*
HUFFPOST Healthy Living Article: Men,
We Don't Take Care of Ourselves, So
What Would Happen If We Did? March
2015

It is helpful to consider a Self Care Plan as an offensive move in every area of your life. To go through life being caught off guard or blindsided by surprises that were avoidable is the life of a man at the mercy of others. Your Self Care Plan includes a balance of wisdom coached to you through a Dream Team Member, step-by-step breakdowns of moves you should make, encouragement from a buddy, recording your goals in a playbook and sharing your successes with trusted friends. This is a formula for preparedness and an invitation to build confidence by learning what you need to move forward in life.

Men need to live healthier lives in every way. Knowing who you are and what you need as a man spiritually, emotionally, economically, physically, educationally and socially is key to not only anchoring yourself, but anchoring your relationships and your community. Consider starting a self-care support group for yourself and those men who aren't interested in hiding from any aspect of their life that needs growth.

> *Our well-being is our most important asset. We cannot live our best life when our health is tenuous. I have a good friend who is now working 2 jobs to meet the demands of providing for his family. As we discussed his ridiculous work hours, I asked him how he was managing the stress he is placing on his body. On que, he said I use the gym and hot tub at my night job to find some relaxation. Whatever the situation, wherever the environment, we must find moments to focus on repairing and preparing our*

bodies to be PRESENT for the years to come. It's a life or death thing! My health and my well-being are my priority. -- Keesonga Juma Gore, Partner, Minott Gore Law Firm

Self Care is an important message for men. It's not that men don't care for themselves, because certainly we do. We could still benefit from an adjustment in our perspective. For example, traditionally men have seen care as "staying strong" physically. And, of course, we want our male sexual parts to function healthily in the long term and to prevent cancer in that area, so we will, begrudgingly, get our prostrate exam. But typically men would rather not go visit doctors, nor typically do we get into the activities that are considered "pampering" by women. Men are witnessing many changes these days. As we continually examine the need for dietary changes, as we continue to "suck it up" and hold our stress deep in our gut and not discuss them as openly as women might, as we become aware of new exercise modes beyond being "big and strong," and even as personal notions of spirituality are being met with new information, then new ideas for Self Care become very valuable. -- Charles DeVeaux

Chapter 3. Implementing a Self Care Plan

Plans are only good intentions unless they
immediately degenerate into hard work.
--Peter Drucker, Management Consultant
and Author

Typically, my personal self-care stories usually begin with me learning the hard way. Whether it's hair care or medical care, I have often in the past found myself dangling without a net or a plan in a critical moment. Creating a Self Care Plan is the first step towards freedom from being at the complete mercy of another person or situation. Quietly, some of us are one paycheck away from being homeless, one tragedy away from losing our minds, one bad meal away from a heart attack, one drink away from a DUI or ending someone's life, one test away from flunking out of school, one reckless sexual behavior away from contracting an incurable illness, one neglectful act away from losing the love of our lives. Now is the time to create a plan customized to your needs and begin taking good care of yourself.

It's very important to not just begin a self-care journey with a good intention, but to have a roadmap, a plan that helps you proactively address your needs on a regular basis. You will soon see, as we delve into each component of the program, that *self-care* doesn't mean *all by yourself.* It means taking baby steps with support and help from those able to help you address your needs, when you need it.

The Self Care Plan Program Components

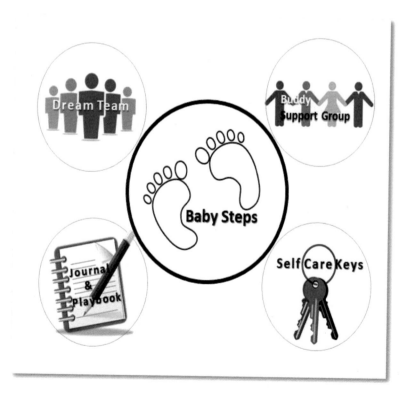

Self Care Dream Team

Why try to accomplish a dream without a Dream Team? Your Dream Team is a group of individuals who specialize in the various areas of self-care. The team can include mentors, experienced and knowledgeable associates, friends or professionals you enlist to focus on your betterment in every category of self-care. You can have more than one Dream Team member per category, if you want. For example, your Physical Care Dream Team members could include a dentist, an OBGYN and your personal trainer.

How should you solicit a Self Care Dream Team member?

More often than not, a Dream Team member that works for you is already passionate about the category of care you are interested in getting guidance on. It will not be necessary to call one up and say, *"Hey will you be my Self Care Dream Team member for educational self-care?"* You can simply ask for specific help with your specific self-care goal. For example, *"Hi, I need some guidance with addressing my student loan issue. Can I schedule a brief phone or in person meeting with you and ask your opinion on what my next step should be?"*

What to do if you're having trouble building a Self Care Dream Team?

Typically trouble building a Self Care Dream Team occurs when we are completely avoiding the task of building one. Fear, worry and embarrassment about being judged for the state of how we have not been caring for ourselves is typically the culprit. Second to fear, worry and embarrassment is lack of exposure to people who would qualify. If this is the case, you first step is to begin researching social outings and information sessions that put you in the company of those who enjoy and are excellent at a particular category of care. Self Care Dream Team Members for one area are also more often than not connected to other individuals who would qualify for other categories of care. Some physicians or yoga instructors may have associates that are excellent at artistic expression or economic development. Ask current Self Care Dream Team Members if they know of others who may be helpful to you in reaching your other goals.

What should you expect from a Self Care Dream Team member?

It is important to have some level of guidance for each category of care, even if it is a category you already enjoy. You should expect your Self Care Dream Team Members to care about your overall self-care and not just their area of expertise. Your Self Care Dream Team Member does not need to be formally announced to have been selected as being you dream team member. Typically they already are working in that particular industry and enjoy sharing and offering advice. They should care about how they talk to you as much as what information and guidance they are offering. They should also be able to be concise and supportive. Your Dream Team member isn't required to hold your hand through every step of your Self Care Plan. Their job is to provide accurate guidance that allows you to work on your plan in their absence. Sometimes selecting a Self Care Dream Team Member is like dating. Some work out and some don't. But don't give up. What should be consistent with every Self Care Dream Team Member is their guidance should lead you towards accomplishing your purpose and reaching your dreams in life.

Self Care Buddy

A Self Care Buddy is a person who agrees to randomly contact you on a regular basis via texting, calling, visiting or private messaging you with a simple question: *How is your self-care going?* This buddy may or may not share his or her personal experiences or opinions with you, but they genuinely care about how you're doing and wait for an answer. Your Self Care Buddy is simply a cheerleader dedicated to supporting you along your self-care journey and is aware of the basic components of a Self Care Plan.

How to Pick a Self Care Buddy

A Self Care Buddy is not always a best friend or close relative. It could be an associate familiar with the Self Care Plan solely interested in your personal success. Your Self Care Buddy is not swayed by worry nor are they judgmental about your answer. Your Self Care Buddy will not attempt to cure you only listen. The main goal of a Self Care Buddy is to bring the topic of your overall self-care to the forefront of your mind and show you that someone does care about you taking care of yourself. A Self Care Buddy will also be sure to not turn the conversation into an opportunity to vent about their own problems. They will ask question -- "How is your self-care going?" You give the answer and your Self Care Buddy will probably provide encouraging words to close out the check-in encounter. Do not make jokes about someone challenges around accomplishing their self-care goal. If you are each other's Self Care Buddy, you may trade off with check-ins in the same call only if you both agree. It is important that the Self Care Buddy who initiated the call give you the space to check in without the obligation to return the favor. This is the strength and true benefit of a Self Care Buddy.

The Self Care Journal and Playbook

Reduce your plan to writing. The moment you complete this, you will have definitely given concrete form to the intangible desire. -- Napoleon Hill

The *Self Care Journal & Playbook* is your primary self-care tool. This two-part tool contains a *journal*, an area where you can write down your feelings on a daily basis, and the *playbook*, your game plan to reaching your self-care goals. According to *The Health Benefits of Journaling* by Maud Purcell, LCSW, and CEAP:

Scientific evidence supports that journaling provides other unexpected benefits. The act of writing accesses your left brain, which is analytical and rational. While your left brain is occupied, your right brain is free to create, intuit and feel. In sum, writing removes mental blocks and allows you to use all of your brainpower to better understand yourself, others and the world around you.

Journaling helps you track your unedited thoughts about how you are taking care of yourself in all areas.

With the Self Care Plan, the only rule is that you aren't allowed to put any pressure on yourself about what you write, when you write, how often you write, and whether or not you share your thoughts with anyone else. When you have a negative thought, a realization about your self- care journey, or a success story to tell, write it down. Visit our website www.selfcareagency.com to obtain your copy of the Self Care Journal and Playbook or the Self Care Check-In Form.

Self Care Planning Keys

The self-care keys are affirmations designed to address critical experiences that might occur during the implementation of a self-care plan. Each key opens the door to a perspective meant to empower you along your way. The keys give you the license and breathing room to continue your challenge with fewer struggles. The negative thoughts, doubts and fears that swim through our mind won't pluck themselves out you have to drown them out with affirmation especially when no one is around. These are the keys:

COURAGE: I have the courage to welcome guidance and support on my self-care journey and release the fear of making mistakes.

WORTHINESS: I reflect, manage, and discuss my worth in a protected space throughout my self-care journey.

INSPIRATION: I place myself in an environment to be inspired and refueled on a regular basis.

FORGIVENESS: I forgive myself for the moments when I don't take good care of myself.

COMMITMENT: I commit to myself to build a foundation of spiritual and emotional support throughout my self-care journey.

PROTECTION: I protect my self-care journey by only sharing my journey with safe and encouraging people and only when I feel it's necessary.

PEACE: I choose to be at peace with the rate at which my self-care plan is progressing and to compassionately share my process when someone in need inquires.

Self Care Revolutionary Assignment: Read the Self Care Keys out loud every day for seven day in a row, morning and night. You have to replace bad thoughts with good ones while on a healing self-care journey.

The idea is to recite these affirmations whenever you need extra spiritual support. You might use the keys as morning affirmations or to check in with your Self Care Buddy or Self Care Dream Team member.

Self Care Baby Steps

The biggest idea in this Self Care Program is that progress happens **one baby step at a time**. Baby steps are called *baby* for a reason. A Self Care Baby Step is any self-care act seeming absurdly simple that gets you closer to accomplishing your self-care goal. Any movement forward is movement forward. There's no pressure to make radical changes. There's no blanket definition for a Self Care Baby Step because what might be a baby step for one person may be a big step for someone else. What may be a Self Care Baby Step in one point of your life may become a big self-care step in another. The key thing to remember is to be gentle to yourself and to start with something that is relatively easy for you to achieve.

For example, if you have a goal to sit still for 15minutes with no phone and eat lunch every day of the week, then your baby step toward that goal could be picking out a space to sit down and eating there at some point in the week, but not actually pressuring yourself to do it *every day*. You might choose to just look at the place one time during the week. Look at the table or the bench or the seat on the balcony with the view and think "one day I will sit and eat in that spot". That is a baby step. Give yourself the week to do it. . Seems absurdly simple right. That is the point and the key to continuously be participating in your own self-care. |#participationnotperfection|

Here are some other examples of a self-care step and then a baby step:

Spiritual

- Praying before (or after) a tough moment
  | Saying pray out loud once

- Meditating for 5 minutes a day | Closing your eyes for 3 seconds
- Visiting a yoga studio (or just finding one near you) | Google yoga
- Listening to 5 minutes of a motivational or inspirational CD that feeds your soul | Pull up one website that may have something motivational on it with no pressure to do anything

Economic

- Finding a financial counselor | Mentioning you need one out loud to someone else
- Finding a webinar on time management | Type time management
- Saying no to one non-priority task | Think of one non-priority task
- Acknowledging your bank account balance today | *Look at an ATM or bank app on your phone

Artistic

- Visit an art gallery | Google 'local art gallery'
- Spending 5 minutes a day writing | Write one sentence about how you really feel
- Staring at a painting or photograph that inspires you | Use your phone and take a picture of something you like.

Physical

- Walking 30 minutes a week | Walk down the hall of your home once
- Parking further away in the parking lot | Look at a faraway parking spot
- Going outside in the middle of the day to get some sun | Find a window and look out the window for 5 seconds

Social

- Shopping at a physical store instead of online | Call someone you like that's selling something you like
- Registering for a dance class you want to take instead of popping in a workout DVD

at home | Drive by a dance studio and look out the window.

- Putting a professional networking function on your calendar| Call someone who frequents networking events and have a general conversation

Education

- Completing the questionnaire in Chapter 2 | Looking at the Questionnaire in Chapter 2
- Making an appointment with a school advisor | Walking past a school advisor's office
- Selecting an online class you want to take | Type a topic and online class in Google but don't hit search

There are two more components of the program that aren't shown in the illustration that I want to talk about here: **Big Steps** and **Self Worth Management.**

Big Steps

While self-care *baby steps* are the essential concept of the program, there will be times on your journey when you will want to take a *big* self-care step. A major shift from your current activity or behaviors that took a lot of energy, focus and courage to make happen is considered a big self-care step. A big self-care step is different for different people based on what is most challenging for each person. When you make a big self-care step, a major shift in your life occurs and your need is addressed in a way that brings more peace, security and direction in your life.

Anana's Big Self Care Step

I remember feeling a lack of confidence in myself after giving birth to my son. The emergency C-section was major surgery and provided some terrifying moments that left me emotionally doubtful about what I could accomplish physically. Before the C-section I was courageous and adventurous. After that traumatic experience, I was cautious and fearful. This was not me. I needed to take emotional and physical self-care steps but didn't know how. I thought about doing something that I didn't think I could handle physically or emotionally and had never done before. I got online and typed *physical courage*. A few things popped up and then I saw it -- a triathlon! I had never done one and had never planned to. I was terrified I would collapse and die halfway through it. When I think back to that moment I saw the advertisement for the triathlon sprint (a shorter version of a main triathlon), I can only laugh to myself at the blind faith and courage I had to sign up for it. A swim in a lake for a mile, a bike ride for 12 miles and, finally, a run for 3.1 miles. My husband at the time was in Afghanistan and I was alone with my 10-month-old son.

The courageous big self-care step part was not signing up for the triathlon nor preparing for it. It was realizing it was happening in two weeks from my sign up time! I would NOT recommend anyone do this. Again, I don't recommend this as a big self-care step with 2 weeks preparation time for anybody. I personally needed to do it and was able to narrowly escape injuring myself. I just needed something to do to believe in myself and my body again. The experience and the surgical incision made me feel weaker than I actual was. The scar tissue felt binding and horrible. So, I bought a bike, went to the YMCA to practice my indoor swimming for the outdoor lake portion (not knowing that wouldn't help). I tried to get others to join me. Surprise! No one did with such short notice. I showed up to the start of the race by myself but not alone. There were mothers, grandmothers, children and others just like me who had made a decision to do something for themselves. The gun fired and I began swimming with lots of other arms and legs splashing around me. After putting in much work I came up for air only to learn the hard way that indoor pool swimming and open water swimming are vastly different. I had barely moved an inch. Most of the splashing arms and legs were gone but I put my head down in the murky water and kept going. I pulled myself out of the water with a celebration that made me feel like a champion.

I glanced past the sand ahead of me only to see a sea of people racing to the parking lot filled with bikes. I joined them only to hop on my bike remaining in the back. Children on bicycles with bells ringed past me during those 12 miles and for a moment I felt a bit defeated. I let that feeling pass and kept going.

With wobbly legs I climbed slowly off the bike and began a long, slow trot with four elderly women fast on my trail for the final 3.1 mile portion of the triathlon. The scenery was beautiful.

I had no idea if I would be able to finish this triathlon. I had to let go of the fact that I wouldn't be first, that it was a sprint and not a full triathlon, that I had to do it alone. I let all of that go because my self-care need was greater than my fears. I needed to do something that my body could succeed at even if I wasn't sure if I could do it. But I did it and

afterward I was different. I was more confident about my body and myself. I wasn't the same as before the C-section, I was *better*. I faced a challenge, survived it then took a big self-care step that I really needed to do to believe in myself.

I cried when I crossed the finish line. No one was there at that moment. I did it anyway. When I look at the pictures now, five years later, I still feel the emotional and physical strength I built on that day.

I am reminded by seeing the photos that if I just keep doing what I can in the moment, I can accomplish anything.

Self Worth Management

Self-worth management is about being aware of how worthy you do or don't feel at a given time. It seems weird to reference as 'management' but you are monitoring and adjusting as the situation or project changes with a constant goal in mind. When you're confident about achieving a self-care goal you've set, your self-worth and self-esteem is probably high.

However, when faced with a challenge, we can sometimes feel embarrassed and worthless while trying to accomplish it. This can sabotage every effort to take better care of ourselves. Without self-worth management, the self-care journey can be a scary and grueling one. Yet, as you empower yourself with making choices as baby steps, and addressing your feelings of self-worth along the way, you will be kinder to yourself when it is most important.

Self-worth management is important because, when you embark on a self-care journey, you may find yourself feeling vulnerable, exposed and unsupported. The reason you may experience difficulty in a particular category of self-care is because something is legitimately challenging for you in that category. The reason you haven't accomplished the goal yet is because it is challenging. It's important to not let feelings of shame or embarrassment stop you from continuing to improve your life spiritually/emotionally, artistically, economically, physically, educationally and socially. All the self-care tools and activities in this book are designed to strengthen your self-worth. You will notice how these feelings of worth will fluctuate as you work your Self

Care Plan. Stick with it. Your feeling of self-worth will increase with every baby and big self-care step.

Listing your needs in each category in the journal, for example, might trigger feelings of low self-worth and make the self-care journey feel almost unbearable. Thoughts like *"I can't believe this is hard for me. I suck for not knowing how to do this already. I am so stupid for not having this figured out already"* can consume us when we are merely writing out our needs. Sensitivities and past pains associated with something as simple as sweeping the floor or checking your daily bank account balance might send you into a corner crying. This is the experience that can be uncovered when you are facing the opportunity for true change. Share it with your Emotional or Spiritual Self Care Dream Team Member and ask for/r guidance.

Self-worth management is about understanding which category(ies) of care make you feel vulnerable, exposed, and embarrassed, then spending time building a healthier perspective of yourself while you address that category of care. For example, if you are focusing on economic self-care (time, money and energy management), you may decide to take the (big) self-care step of asking for an adjustment to your work schedule that will allow you to make it to the gym on a regular basis. When you prepare to walk into your supervisor's office, you must bring a solid vision and belief of your worth with you.

Here are some activities you can use to help strengthen your self-worth before the meeting:

Tools: Your journal, a pen, and a mirror. Look at yourself in the mirror. Give yourself three compliments. Say them out loud. Then, write them down in your journal. Read them aloud.

Dress in something that makes you feel wonderful for the meeting.

Tools: Magazines, poster board, glue, scissors. Go through the stack of magazines and cut out images of people, places, and things that represent you, your talents, and your aspirations. Make a self-worth collage. Hang it in your bedroom or bathroom. Take a few minutes to **enjoy** these images first thing in the morning every day for at least a week before your meeting.

Looking in the mirror, recite this affirmation three times: I am a confident person worthy of meeting my own needs. I believe in myself and nothing can stop me from reaching my life goals.

Knowing you are worthy before diving into a big self-care act is critical to a positive outcome in the long run.

Taking a Big Self Care Step

As you move along this journey of establishing a self-care lifestyle, your momentum will pick up, your confidence will build, and soon you will want to make a big self-care step. Baby steps tend to snowball into larger more impactful results that train your thoughts and actions into building a stronger self-care muscle while believing more and more in yourself.

There is something powerful and enlightening about taking a big self-care step. It exposes your soft underbelly and the strength of your spine at the same time. Don't run from a big self-care step. Just continue to update and review your worth.

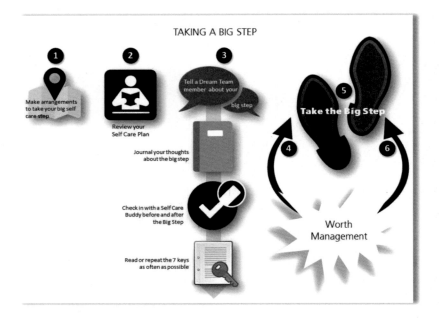

TAKING A BIG STEP

1. Make arrangements to take your big self care step

2. Review your Self Care Plan

3. Tell a Dream Team member about your big step

Journal your thoughts about the big step

Check in with a Self Care Buddy before and after the Big Step

Read or repeat the 7 keys as often as possible

5. Take the Big Step

Worth Management

Follow these steps when you want to make a big self-care step:

1. Prepare to take your big self-care step
   - List your core needs.
   - Request the time of those who can help you reach your goal.
2. Review your Self Care Plan
   - Read your needs and self-care goals in every category.
3. Get the support you need:

- Tell a dream team member about your big step.
- Journal your thoughts about the big step.
- Check in with a Self Care Buddy before and after the big self-care step.
- Read or intone the 7 Self Care Keys as often as possible.

4. Complete your Self Worth Management activities before the big step.
5. Implement the big self-care step.
6. Complete your Self Worth Management activity again.

Even though the illustration emphasizes a Self Worth Management tool, you really use *all* the tools both before and after the big step.

Big Step Scenario Using the 6 Steps

Here is an example of using the six-step Big Step.

Prepare to take your big self-care step.

- List your core needs: I need to know what I owe. I need to know any critical deadlines coming up. I need the contact information to the lending institution. I need a Self Care Dream Team Member who can help with this.

- Request the time of those who can help you reach your goal: I will call my friend who successfully set up a payment plan for his student loans and ask that he share his advice on what my next steps should be.

Review your Self Care Plan.

Read your needs and self-care goals in every category: My spiritual and emotional goals are to feel more at peace. My loans not being addressed stress me out quietly. My artistic goals are to paint more. My physical goals are to get more sleep and stop waking up worrying about things in the middle of the night. My economic goals are to spend my time more wisely and reap a larger return on the work I am able to do. My educational goals are to qualify for more grants and aid to help further my education. I am missing a Self Care Dream Team Member for economic self-care so I should start looking for one that also is familiar with student loans.

Get the support you need.

- Tell a Self Care Dream team member about your big step: I told my friend my goal is to set up payments for my student loans.
- Journal your thoughts about the big step: I am terrified the final balance is higher than I last check and I don't want to see it. I also will be so embarrassed if my friend thinks I'm stupid for not having this handled already.
- Check in with a Self Care Buddy before and after the big self-care step: I called my Self Care Buddy and told them what I was about to do. They encouraged me and didn't think I was stupid.
- Read the 7 Self Care Keys as often as possible. I hung them in the mirror and rad them to myself while brushing my teeth in the mornings.

Complete your Self-Worth Management activities before the big step.

I journaled my true feelings before my meeting and asked for encouragement from my Dream Team Member.

Implement the big self-care step.

Complete your Self Worth Management activity again.

I journaled my true feelings after the meeting was over. I really did it and can push forward to continue getting more done.

Gathering Your Self Care Tools

Don't wait until you have all your tools gathered before you start the plan. You don't have to have a Self Care Buddy or a Dream Team before you get started on your plan. The fundamental tools are:

- A journal, where you can post or record your thoughts and
- the Self Care Check In Form that lists all the categories of care

While the official *Self Care Playbook and Journal* is easily available online, you can really use anything as a journal, like a notebook or even loose paper. You can find the Self Care Challenge Form at www.selfcaregency.com. More than anything, to start the plan, you need the *desire* to make a change in your life.

Participation NOT Perfection

The more you participate in the plan, the stronger your self-care muscle gets and the more challenges you will want to face. Participation puts you in the company of other encouragers and continuously builds your confidence. Your time is your time. It is not a race. It's your life. For some challenges, participation will be easy. One category of care will be a breeze and another may feel like diving out of an airplane. Don't be embarrassed and don't feel *less than* if something is easy for someone else and hard for you. Letting go of self judgement may turn out to be one of the hardest things you learn to do while on the self-care journey. Just keep participating. Find a Self Care Buddy. Be a Self Care Buddy. Get a support team. Be part of a support team. If you want to. The more you participate, the more you learn. Don't give up on *you*.

Dealing with Other People

When family, friends, co-workers and others resist your new lifestyle, do your best to continue to stick to your plan. Your Self Care Plan is not indulgent activity filled with frivolous tasks. It is linked to your sanity and your critical, holistic needs.

When you begin to shift your lifestyle to one that incorporates more self-care, you will start to see a change in your behavior and in the behavior of those around you. Take your time. Don't rush your process. When others around you turn up the heat to take you off your new path, allow your Self Care Plan to turn up as well. Use your Self Care Buddy, your Dream Team and your Self Care Support Group to keep you strong.

For example, if you have decided to stop automatically saying *yes*, without checking your schedule to everyone who invites you to an event, you will see that your *new* response has shifted from one of pleasing the asker immediately to one in which you think about your self-care goals first. In time, you will even release any guilt around saying *no* or around not always making yourself available for everybody else's needs. The guilt will begin to subside one self-care act at a time and you will see people live through your self-care decision making.

Good Voice, Bad Voice

Often, when you're working on self-care, a voice in your head may come up with a good idea, like "drink three glasses of water today." Then another voice might say, "No wait; you'll have to run out in the middle of your meeting with your manager to get to the bathroom." How do you deal with these kinds of thoughts, positive and negative?

According to Shelley Chapman, a healthy lifestyle expert, if it's a thought in your head, good or bad, it is *valid.* Valid or not, doubtful thoughts are cancerous. Unchecked, they grow and contaminate practically everything. When doubtful or negative thoughts arise immediately after courageous ones, the best thing you can do is apply a Negative Thought Action Plan.

A Negative Thought Action Plan is comprised of the following steps:

Brain Dump. Journal all your thoughts in your Self-Care Journal.

Ask for Help. Ask for encouragement and guidance from any support groups you may have and from your Self Care Dream Team members.

Baby Steps. Assign yourself a Self-Care baby step from each category, for balance.

Forgive Yourself. Forgive yourself for not being perfect and release any shame.

Keep it Moving. Stay focused and faithful by working your Self-Care Plan.

To test this idea, take the issue you are most afraid of right now and create an affirmation that counters it specifically. Say the affirmation out loud everyday as many times as you can. For example:

Negative thought: *My stomach pokes out in all my clothes and, when the wind blows, I look five months pregnant, even when I try to hold my stomach in. I look terrible.*

Affirmation: *I am beautiful just the way I am and my body is healthy.*

We are more than our bodies and we are beautiful holistically. If we only acknowledge even one part of our body as a horrible thing, we must affirm our *whole beauty* until that positive affirmation counters the negative one.

Negative thought: *I feel stupid walking into a room when I don't know anyone. I don't know what to say and will probably look like an idiot.*

Affirmation: *I am genuine and at peace with myself in all environments and in all conversations.*

Feeling comfortable with who we are allows us to walk into a room without judgment of ourselves or of others.

Being preoccupied with worrying about someone thinking you are stupid or attempting to embarrass you changes how you choose to present yourself. This also makes it hard to truly hear what someone is saying because their words are trapped in your assumption that they think you are stupid. To be genuine is to be able to say *I don't know* when you don't know.

Creating Your Own Self Care Strategy

When we decide to dedicate our lives to growing a business, we develop a strategy and a plan. No matter how loose or subconscious the strategy, one is created and adjusted to meet the goal of having a business. A business that wants to stay open and flourish will find a way to be flexible and keep very specific frameworks in place which include address the critical needs of the business. It is a strategy to review the needs and recognize moments when the needs a not getting met. Creating a Self Care Strategy to compliment your overall Self Care Plan is really about regular assessment of changing needs in a strategic way. For instance, a foody that does not include food in their personal Self Care Strategy is not being strategic and realistic.

If you are truly ready to develop your own Self Care Strategy, here is what you need to repeat on a regular basis.

1. Ask yourself *regularly* the following,
- [BLOCK]   Do I Have a Block?
- [LOOP]   Am I Stuck in a Loop?

- [PLAN] Am I Sticking to My Self Care Plan?
2. Only speak about your critical self-care needs with those who are supportive.
3. Participation not Perfection is the Strategy.
4. Make your Self Care Strategy & Plan VISIBLE.

For this to be a strategic move customized for you, put these words 'BLOCK LOOP PLAN' somewhere visible to YOU. Hang it by your mirror in a frequently used bathroom with a list of your Self Care Goals nearby. Schedule this list of questions to pop up on your calendar once a week. This is a strategy customized for you. What do YOU need to continue *paying attention* to your Self Care Goals and Plan?

Self Care Blocks

Many times we beat up on ourselves for not accomplishing goals quicker, sooner or even at all. Cleaning up our credit or our house, getting a degree, getting in shape, getting a new job, starting a business, spending more time with family and friends or traveling the world. When beginning to think about a

Self Care Goal, immediately thoughts of shame, embarrassment and anxiety can pop up if that particular goal has been challenging to maintain or accomplish. Not only do we beat up on ourselves, we also listen to and absorb haphazardly made, blanketed, damaging and judgmental statements beginning with, 'why don't you just ...' or 'women always...' ... or 'men always.. or 'black people never...' These bandwagon harmful statements can fuel negative emotions that create Self Care Blocks. When the thought of taking better care of yourself passes your mind, you may feel challenged for a legitimate reason. Legitimately, something is occurring internally or externally to make it harder or to stop you all together from taking care of yourself. Something from your childhood, missing resources, imagining the worst outcome or completely avoiding an argument could be a very natural block. Judge it if you want to, but it is there. This occurrence, this feeling, this response is a block. For example, if you *need* to drink more water, look at a faucet or bottle of drinkable water and walk away, something made you walk away. That something exists. If you look at your bank account, need to make more money and not do something immediately or in your day to work towards making more money, something is blocking your self-care choice to do so. Acknowledging that you do walk away is a big deal and the first step. Once it is clear what you need and that you are choosing to walk away from what you need, the next step is to find a way to get help and learn how to help yourself meet your own needs on a regular basis.

Trained therapists, counselors and coaches who administer therapy in the way that is healthiest for you are always a wonderful resource to have. What do we do when a therapist is not around? What do we do when a financial adviser, a physician, a pastor or a life coach is not available? What do we do when the feeling that moves us farther away from reaching our Self Care Goal is real, immediate and reoccurring? A therapist may assist you in figuring that out and healing whatever open wound is triggered when you try to make self-care choices. What do we do in the meantime and how do we not isolate ourselves to death?

As stated earlier, first, pay attention to *when* a Self Care Block happens and what that block feels like. To remain active in your own Self Care Strategy, it is most important to pay attention the moment it happens.

Remember, the feelings you feel are valid whether they are blocking you from taking care of yourself or not. When those feelings are so severe your safety and wellbeing is in jeopardy, ask for help immediately as a healthy critical self-care response. There are certain words that can help define what a Self Care Block can look like for you. Some of these words can easily overlap. For the purpose of this book and Self Care Strategy format, let's look at the following words as triggers and/or terms that can arise when we begin to try and accomplish a Self Care Goal.

Avoiding an Argument or Confrontation

Whether you are at work, in a romantic relationship, a friendship, engaging with family or walking down the street, avoiding an argument can easily trump a self-care decision. You may feel fear, exhaustion, and lack of hope or basic frustration when thinking about talking to someone about a critical self-care need. You see the need and choose to ignore it merely because you do not want an argument. If this happens once, it is not a critical response. If you ignore your critical self-care needs to avoid an argument on a regular basis with one or multiple people, avoiding an argument is placed at a higher priority that meeting in your critical self-care need. That my friend, is unacceptable. Your feeling is legitimate and a complete shut down in the category of care you are ignoring just to avoid an argument is inevitable. Avoiding an argument is a Self Care Block.

"This is unfair" Thoughts

Thinking about working out after having a baby, or recovering from some traumatic event may trigger a thought like, "This is really unfair I have to deal with this amount of discomfort and pain." This thought alone is enough for some to completely deter them from working on a Self Care Goal. Is it legitimate? Do your feelings matter? Yes. Will you ever reach you Self Care Goal by allowing this thought to turn you around each time? No. True or not, this thought needs to be replaced with the Self Care Thought/affirmation "This is possible, one Self Care Baby Step at a time."

False Comfort

False comfort is a Self Care Block when we tell ourselves an act is more comforting than achieving a critical Self Care Goal. For instance, lying in bed an extra ten minutes in the morning and telling yourself getting an extra 10 minutes of sleep is more comforting than ending the pain in your back or neck is letting False Comfort block you for the self-care act of making an appointment with a doctor or healer. Sleep will not end physical pain better than healing the actual injury. Watching television or scrolling through social media will add false comfort if the real comfort you critical need is a gentle, safe, warm loving hug. False comfort is block because the minimal comfort you think you are receiving is laid on top of a painful and consistent pain that needs to be addressed immediately.

Fear

Of course this is that good old fashion bottom line reason for running in the other direction every time. Fear truly is the root of almost every Self Care Block however to separate it and name it means you have to counter balance this particular Self Care Block with the only act that can face it and defeat it, courage. Ask for help generating the courage. Watch a movie or documentary that exhibits a characters courage. Call fear wat it is. Pride can keep us from being honest at time. Say out loud, "I am afraid that _____" and watch the exact courageous self-care move you need to do begin to take shape. Fear can be surrounded, smothered and destroyed one Self Care Baby Step at a time.

Imagining Perceived Discomfort and Pain

This Self Care Block is a time stealer and stress generator. Sitting around imagining the discomfort and pain you THINK may happen if you start to take care of yourself in a particular way is not only a waste of time but an affective Self Care Block. This block requires creativity, time, energy and sometimes an audience to laugh at how funny it would be when you try and fail. Yes, imagining discomfort and pain may seem harmless as a Self Care Block until you stumble upon doing it over and over and over again. "I bet my back will hurt worse." I probably can only last 10 seconds." "I am sure I will look ridiculous." Change your thoughts when you begin to see this Self Care Block occurring. This level of negative imagination is blocking you from accomplishing a Self Care Goal.

Embarrassment

Feeling embarrassed can be a crippling experience especially when each new experience is tied to a past one that also didn't feel good. Fear is tied to embarrassment however embarrassment more often than not involves other people witnessing failure. It almost seems impossible and unrealistic to 'get over' feeling embarrassed. What a Self Care Strategy offers is the opportunity to first acknowledge what you are embarrassed about that is blocking you from a self-care activity then customizing a plan to address the embarrassment with what you NEED. This block can be pushed through. Work the plan, take Self Care Baby Steps and find the right environment/people to encourage you through to completion without ridicule.

A.F.D. and Tunnel Loop

The Analyze, Fuss & Discuss Loop is a critical component of asking '*Am I Stuck in a Loop*?' After learning a certain way of responding to crisis or even normal everyday experiences, we tend to get 'stuck in a loop' while talking about working on our Self Care Goals. For instance, it is healthy to self-analyze what may be challenging about a self-care act, fuss a bit about it then call a friend to discuss it. It is not healthy to repeat that process over and over again so much so that you never actually accomplish the Self Care Goal.

An A.F. D. Loop example:

Self Care Goal: Go to dance class. It helps my physical self-esteem.

Action: Call a Friend or Type in a Social Media Message/Post the following

Analyze – A factual expression of what goes through your mind when you think about accomplishing a Self Care Goal.

"I typically don't go to dance classes as much because my C-section experience was so traumatic that I am emotionally reminded of it every time I go. I also am not as aerobically in shape and I used to be and I feel embarrassed to not be able to dance the way I would like to."

Fuss – Honest emotion filled pouring out of feeling around what is upsetting and frustrating about having to accomplish a Self Care Goal. No listening is happening just dumping of true real time emotions.

"I am so pissed when I show up and everyone asks 'where have you been?' or asks really personal questions I can't answer without crying. It's hard enough to get out of the house and make it let alone having to explain myself or worse pretend like I'm ok all the time."

Discuss – Contact someone to speak analysis, fuss and listen to feedback or ideas.

"Hey what do you think? I need to feel good again dancing and going is how that will happen so what do you think? (Response) Yes but... I know but... Ok thanks. I'll let you know if I end up doing it."

The problem is not that a person will analyze, fuss and discuss about a particular issue. The problem is when you restart this loop over and over again, day in and day out to the same or different people. Is there a reason why? Of course there is a reason why? Are your feelings legitimate? Of course your feelings are legitimate. Is repeating this loop over and over again keeping you from accomplishing your Self Care Goal? Being stuck in an A.F.D. Loop is absolutely stopping you from reaching your Self Care Goal.

How do you break an A.F.D. Loop? One Self Care Baby Step at a Time.

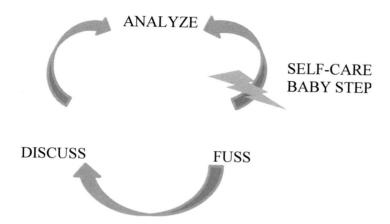

Chapter 4. Starting a Self Care 30 Day Challenge

We are what we repeatedly do. Excellence then, is not an act, but a habit. -- Aristotle

The purpose of a 30 Day Self Care Challenge is to integrate the Self Care Plan into your life over the course of 30 days, focusing on a specific goal. This gives you a chance to really look at how you do and don't take care of yourself; to find your pain points, and to slowly, gently, move your life towards better self-care. You may choose to do the challenge alone or with a group of other Self Care advocates. Either way, what's important to remember is the purpose of the challenge is *participation* and not *perfection*.

Day One

1. By now, if you have been using the *Self Care Journal & Playbook*, you have your Self Care Plan documented. You've listed

your Self Care Buddy(ies), your Dream Team members. You have the Seven Keys handy. You listed some goals that you want to reach for each of the categories of care. For now, just review your Self Care Plan. Just look at it. Take it in.

2. Post or journal a message when you can.
3. Check in with a Buddy.
4. Ask for help to accomplish your critical Self-Care areas, if you need it.

Pick *One* Goal in *One* Category:

Use the table here to pick one goal in one category that you want to focus on for 30 days. Each goal has a suggested activity for you to do during the challenge. You may, however, choose something entirely different. These are provided simply to help get your thoughts and ideas flowing.

Overall Self Care Goals

Category	Goal	Activity
Spiritual/ Emotional	*Become more in touch with my spiritual and emotional needs*	***Consistent Journaling****: You pick the frequency and length, but consistency is the challenge.*

	and experiences.	*Weekly Spiritual/Emotional Check In*: Pick an especially safe Self Care Dream Team member like a pastor, spiritual supporter or a counselor and check in regularly during the entire challenge.
Economic	Become aware of and research guidance around my economic state.	**Evidence Revealed**: Record your time, money and energy distribution over 30 days. **The Value of Values**: Develop an honest value list that may include items like financial stability family or mate approval; proving someone wrong, financial freedom, peaceful decision making. Review or add to the list every day of the challenge.
Artistic	Allow artistic experiences to open up my creative side and provide a healing experience when needed.	**Artistic Witness**: At least once a week over the 30 days, witness others fully express their artistry through various mediums. **Creative Medicine**: At least once a week over the 30 days, write one paragraph about something you experienced, then express your emotions around it in a chosen art form.
Physical	Become aware of my actual physical needs and	**Assess to Win**: Schedule an appointment with a physician or certified holistic practitioner

	address the most critical areas.	and get a complete assessment of your physical health. **Priorities on Display**: Display the top three items that could help address your most critical areas and read them out loud each day for the entire challenge.
Social	Become aware of my anxieties and explore social options that address my needs.	**Different Room, Different Thought**: Record your voice, or write down what you feel like walking into different rooms: a room full of high powered executives and business owners, a room full of artists, dancers and singers; a room full of rich investors, a room full of spiritual gurus and pastors, a room full of PhD's, attorneys and politicians; a room full of financial experts; a room full of family members you like, a room full of family members you don't like, a room full of children. **Do I Know What I Need?**: Other people can help us reach our goals. Spend the challenge brainstorming and writing down what you may need and how others may help.

		Helpful Environment: Research organizations that encourage and support individual's growth based on your particular area of need.
Educational	Examine my values and create an educational plan.	Knowledge is Power: Knowing what you valu and are passionate about can fuel your journey, so regularly write words or sentences th express your values and passions. Plan to Succeed: Schedule interviews with individuals who are knowledgeable about educational planning. Attend at least one meeting and ask two question

Highly Focused Self Care 30-Day Challenges

For your 30-Day Challenge, you may want to zoom in on a more specific challenge in a particular area, like any of the examples following:

Physical	No refined sugar
Social	No cursing
Social/Education	No television
	& or the internet
Spiritual	No self criticizing
Spiritual	No judging others
Physical/Social	Go out at least once a ˙
Physical	No fast food or alcohc
Spiritual	Read an affirmation
	loud every day

There is no perfect result. Use the Self Care Plan form found on www.selfcareagency.com to assist in recording your Self-Care baby steps, Self Care Dream Team members, and to use as a reminder. Some days the best participation in your Self-Care journey you may be able to come up with is looking at the form, and that's just fine.

When negative thoughts arise during your 30-day challenge, work on implementing the Negative Thought Action Plan we discussed earlier.

The challenge is a sacred time that will expose many things, like how you prioritize, how you communicate, and the rapport you have built with those around you based on your existing self-care habits and decision-making.

It takes a lot of courage to accept the Self Care Challenge. During this time, you may find that you want to put people (and life in general!) on hold, because the idea of integrating them would mean something significant would change. How you prioritize what you choose to do in the course of each day may change. The way you interact with others may change. The good news is all of these things may change for the better.

Repetition of the same thought or physical action develops into a habit which, repeated frequently enough, becomes an automatic reflex -- Norman Vincent Peale

People do not decide their futures, they decide their habits and their habits decide their futures -- FM Alexander

Chapter 5: Personal and Family Self Care

Who will teach us about caring for ourselves holistically if not the people we began life with? Personal and family self-care means that all the needs of the family are integrated with the needs of the individual. An ideal scenario would have each member of the family use the Self-Care Program to address his or her own needs. For inspiration, the family would gather to discuss self-care success stories and lovingly support each other along the way.

Our parents, theoretically, are supposed to teach us everything we need to survive and hopefully thrive in life. Unfortunately, we aren't all blessed with active parents and even the active ones weren't handed instruction manuals during or after the birthing process. How do parents know how to teach self-care balance if they themselves weren't taught?

Analyzing the definition of *successful* parenting is a hot bed topic widely argued and often distorted. Because of the many variances of circumstances we all live in, this book is focused on proactively working with what you have and allowing your spiritual and emotional dream team to help you work through personal circumstances.

Religious communities, family members, professionals and friends tend to help along the way, yet it can sometimes seem like a tangled web of advice when a difficult time surfaces. As we move through our adult life and spend time processing our past, handling our present and planning for our future, it can feel down right impossible to get a good rhythm of balanced self-care going. If we are blessed, self-care angels float into our lives and bring gold nuggets of lessons to add to our self-care manual.

Anana's Self Care Angel Story

During my sophomore year at Howard University, I stayed in the Slowe Hall dormitory and met what soon became one of my dearest friends and self-care angels, then, Chemistry major and now Dr. Michelle Hawkins-Aguilar. I had just finished washing my hair and, with my door open, hair dripping wet, she passed by my room. Out of the corner of her eye, she saw me put a hot curling iron on my dripping wet, permed hair. It snapped, crackled and popped like a bowl of cereal in stereo as the actual steam fogged up my slender dorm room mirror. Michelle almost stumbled and moon-walked backwards in sheer horror at the torture I was putting my hair follicles through. She screamed, "what are you doing!!??" I rolled my former tom boy eyes like I had learned to do oh so well and said with great attitude and flare, "I'm drying my hair." I thought to myself, "What is her problem? She's needs to move on'. As far as I was concerned, I had figured out an ingenious way of drying my hair by skipping the blow drying step and going straight to curling. I mean, heat was heat right? Why hadn't Madam CJ Walker thought of this before me? My way saves a lot of time and allows me to get on with my day.

It was the first time I tried this hair-brained scheme (pun intended). Although she had never been in a physical public fight a day in her life (contrary to *my* background), Michelle decided to get quite assertive and reached for the flat iron in superhero fashion while saying, "You are going to burn your hair off your head!"

First of all, I thought, "who does this girl think she is?" Then, I looked in her eyes only to see the focus of a diving eagle ready to pounce on its prey if I placed that curling iron on my soaking wet hair one more time. I figured since she looked so serious I would oblige her and listen to a different idea.

That day was the beginning of me learning more about how to take care of one small portion of me -- my hair, and I have my dear best friend Michelle to thank for it. She chose to change the course of her day and cared enough to explain to me how to better care for myself.

When we aren't taught how to care for ourselves in a particular area of our life, we are like children: at five feet nine inches, I felt six years old learning how to care for my hair at the age of nineteen. Later in life, after having coordinated a Howard Homecoming fashion show with a five figure budget at age 21, I still felt ten years old when an accountant reviewed my personal finances for the first time. The point is, no matter how advanced we are in one particular area of our lives, we should never ignore the areas in which we still need to learn how to better care for ourselves in. Accept the caring help when it's offered.

When it comes to understanding your current self-care habits, the formula is the same. Who taught you how to take care of yourself spiritually/emotionally, economically, artistically, physically, educationally and socially? When you have a pending crisis at work, who gave you examples on how to best take care of yourself through it? When your bank account is lower than you want it to be, who taught you how to adjust your lifestyle so you can have greater financial security? When you need a more creative approach to networking with a new crowd of people, who taught you how to effect a winning conversation with a new business prospect? When your body or spirit has faced an unimaginable trauma, who taught you how to recover from that? When you need to learn a new skill, who taught you how to learn well? When you are feeling courageous in an unfamiliar area, whose behavior do you reference when making the next step?

Whether your friends are closer to you than you blood relatives, use the family network that exists to support your self-care goals

The Accidental Self Care Manual

Each of us has recorded a self-care manual all on our own, but, by accident. In terms of self-care, we have witnessed individuals growing up who have specific self-care practices and that we have never forgotten. Good or bad, we have accidentally programmed a self-care manual based on what we've been exposed to. A parent's way of discussing finances becomes our way - -accidentally. An aunt's way of expressing herself artistically becomes what we see as artistic self-care. A cousin's way of working out consistently becomes our understanding of physical self-care.

The contrary is also true. You may have an uncle whose teeth were rotting out of his mouth and he's never focused on his dental health, only to lose his teeth early in life. This becomes your visual understanding of low self-care.

Some parents skip ever taking a balanced approach to teaching self-care lessons to their children and focus on the major areas like, personal hygiene, saving money in a piggy bank or protecting yourself from a bully at school. By teaching a child how to pay attention to more than just one category of self-care, you are teaching them to honor all of who they are and what they need.

A great book that helps demystify unhelpful self-care programming is called *The Four Agreements*. The author, Don Miguel Ruiz, beautifully and succinctly outlines how we make agreements or contracts with ourselves that we have to deprogram in order to get beyond blocks in our life. Reading his book is a great self-care assignment.

Try this exercise. Name a person from your earliest memory who, in your opinion, took excellent care of his or her self? Write this person's name here:

_____

_____

What did she do that made you feel she took such good care of herself? How did you see or perceive her getting ready in the morning or preparing for bed at night? What was consistent in her life? How did she handle difficulty and success? Describe a moment when you knew for sure that this person took good care of his or her self spiritually, economically, artistically, physically, educationally and socially.

_____

_____

_____

_____

_____

_____

Now, name a person you witnessed growing up who, in your opinion, took horrible care of himself.

_____

_____

How did you see or perceive him getting ready in the morning? What did he do that made you feel he took such horrible care of himself? How did he handle difficulty and success? Describe a spiritual, economic, artistic, physical, educational or social interaction you had with him.

_____

_____

_____

_____

Take a moment to share your thoughts in your self-care group or with a self-care. This small exercise is not about judgment. Instead, focus on what you learned or felt.

The exercise illustrates a few things. Your memories may hold a key to how you have been making decisions regarding your self-care habits or lack thereof. For example, I have no recollection of being taught hair care principles nor what to do to recover from being stitched up after surgery. Some decisions are based on what you determined you will *never* do and some are based on having no idea at all of what to do.

With each milestone our lives, our bodies and minds adjust to the neglect we've put them through until one day, our low level self-care methods are not enough to help us recover from a trauma or a difficult experience. Life happens -- the death of a loved one or a loss of a job, and we pull from the only self-care methods we've been taught.

The methods we use to take care of ourselves matter. We matter. Whether it's through a story about someone in your cultural or family heritage taking care of themselves through adversity or a friend you meet along the way in life who personifies resilience, we can learn how to recover from challenges while being inspired.

What tends to be missing in most self-care lessons we accidentally experience in life is *balance*. You may have excellent self-care habits in the area of spirituality and socializing, but not in the areas of financial management. You may be a wonderful budget balancer and revenue generator but your creative side suffers. You may know how to excel academically but you are missing emotional compassion for others in need. In this book, we describe self-care tools like a Self Care Journal, Self Care Plan Baby Step tracking, and a Self Care Dream Team to regularly address your needs holistically.

We could spend our entire lifetime and thousands of dollars on counseling to find the root of our behaviors, and it would be more than helpful.

You may choose to seek a professional to hold your hand and walk backwards with you to a time when you may have had less control than you do now. Asking for help and guidance is a wonderful self-care act. However, the program described in this book is not about psychoanalyzing your past. That is the job of a trained therapist. In fact, the previous exercise is the only reaching back to your childhood I suggest.

In addition to examining and healing from our past, it is also important to arm ourselves with self-care tools that service our present day needs and help us move forward one day at a time. With that in mind, this book was written to gently offer a place to focus the development of a self-care plan customized to your needs that compliment your current life goals. Look at self-care as a way to nurture yourself while growing. Establishing your own habits of self-care is how you will handle the fluctuations of life.

Today you may feel wonderfully taken care of and tomorrow something could happen that may knock the wind out of you and shift your focus to completely neglect your critical self-care needs. This book is meant to help you create a soothing self-care rhythm by helping you to develop self-care tools, environments and teams for support, when the need exists. Having a lifestyle based in self-care helps you better address trauma, issues at work, and pop-up family challenges that can feel all-consuming. Telling your self-care story in a group setting can help you get acknowledged for all the good you have done to care for yourself. There is power in telling and sharing your story. It frees you and inspires others. Have the courage to be a blessing.

What are your self-care needs? Let's find out together. Complete the Self Care Questionnaire in the Appendix to complete a self-care check-in.

Self Care in Relationships

Recording and addressing what you discover about taking care of yourself is an act of building an intimate relationship with yourself. There is a sweet spot in you that, when you touch it as an act of self-care, you create a feeling of tenderness and safety at the same time. The opportunity to be intimate with yourself is by far the greatest gift you can get from the Self Care Matters text, journal and playbook.

Intimacy is about closeness, and about having the courage to consistently get in touch with your own needs. This will help you improve the relationship you have with yourself and, as a result, with others. The things you really need to *feel* better and *do* better will slowly become more and clearer to you.

You will discover what kinds of things are hard for you to do and what things are scary for you to do. You will need more time and more compassion to accomplish them and that's OK. Being tender and compassionate with yourself when addressing challenging need is like smiling while gently caressing a sore spot on your body that needs touch to heal. It may hurt a little and remind you of what caused the pain, but if you smile anyway and stay gentle, you can control the pressure and frequency of the healing rub. You can even decide to stop rubbing that sore spot and return to it later. You make a sacred connection with yourself when you caress a painful area of your life. Real intimacy is born out of moments like this. First learning what you need is an intimate experience. Next, sharing what you need with another person is also a way to build intimacy and trust.

Protect your self-care journey every step of the way and when you feel strong enough, share some of your goals and needs with someone you trust. This can be a wonderful tool for enhancing an important relationship in your life. Parents and children, husbands and wives, best friends and romantic partners can use this program to check in and learn more about each other's needs. All of the self-care goals you write down are for you to accomplish. The act of sharing your needs is merely a step towards closeness with another person.

Quite often we believe our lack of a self-care is not obvious to others. Skipping a meal here and being passively silent there can seem like small acts if they only happen every now and then. But a habit of low self-care can bring unimaginable stress on a relationship and trigger intense feelings of disappointment or even jealously towards the other person.

I remember a moment early in my marriage when I realized that I was flat out jealous of my husband. He always seemed to take good care of himself. Unlike me, if we were running late for something, he never skipped a shower or a meal so that we could be on time. One day, I decided to have a day where I responded just as my husband did, with ultimate self-care.

It was a Sunday and it was time to go to church. We didn't have our son at that time, so I leisurely woke up and took a calm shower. Normally, I would awaken him and remind him a few times of the deadline to walk out of the door and make it on time. But, on this day, I chose to remember he was an adult who didn't need to be managed. I chose to gently remind him, then immediately focus on my self-care. The shower was wonderful. I didn't take a very long one, but I do remember vividly not thinking about the time.

I got out of the shower, made us some breakfast and peacefully got dressed. While waiting for my husband, I grabbed a journal, sat on our bedroom balcony, and soaked up some much-needed vitamin D. As my skin said thank you, I heard rumbling in the kitchen – he was grabbing some food. I leaned back in the chair and said with a smile, "I'm ready whenever you are". It was so different. I was at peace and we were late for church. I chose to take care of myself. No buildings fell as a result of us walking in after the choir started the opening song. The message was still powerful and I did not pass out. This was amazing. I finished my entire twenty four hours with no major crises. My husband was baffled all day long. I was completely opposite of my multitasking rushing to accomplish everything self.

My little self-care exercise had nothing to do with bashing him for his self-care choices. He did not protest. My exercise had *everything* to do with me giving myself a self-care assignment that helped me practice making my critical need for peace of mind during my day a priority while simultaneously doing my best to meet all of my obligations. When I *stopped* owning my responsibility to care for myself, resentment towards my husband's ability to not stress about time grew. Well after this exercise my resentment dramatically decreased and I was able to understand better the gift of self-care he exhibited so well for that aspect of his life.

Now, I am very keen on recognizing that meeting my own needs is an integral way to enhance my relationships at work, home and play. Whether it's a spouse, child, friend or co-worker, caring for yourself ultimately improves every dealing you have with them every single time.

It is a good example of the adage that we've all heard from a flight attendant or read on the safety card: *always put your oxygen mask on first, then check on the person in the seat next to you.*

Chapter 6: Self Care for Moms

One of the most difficult challenges I had to handle in becoming a new mom was feeling guilty for trying to address my self-care needs at a time when my son had needs as well. The disconnect from knowing what I needed immediately impacted my ability to be a good mother. As most mothers know, with only 24 hours in a day, you can truly only accomplish so much. Most of the time in my case, especially in the early days of breast feeding and diaper land, I rarely addressed my own self-care. If I wasn't caught in the throes of feeling the pain of first time breastfeeding, then it was the horrible feeling of shuffling around like a tub of unwanted cellulite and gas. That's what took up most of my non-baby attention. Self-care in the first few weeks after giving birth felt more like survival of the fittest.

People will preach self-care to you as a mother but not many will show you how to do it in a way that applies to your specific circumstances. When I got well-intentioned suggestions like "sleep when he sleeps", my immediate thought was, *so when do I eat?* To say I was lost and frustrated would be the understatement of the year.

As mothers grow more and more stressed, they often cling to coping methods that are *familiar* but incomplete and that ultimately disconnect them from their true feelings. Methods like eating to feel better and retreating from social activity due to exhaustion or a drop in self-esteem are legitimate responses to stress, but not true self-care approaches.

In reality, I hadn't consulted enough people with wisdom to know what I needed. Scrambling around like I did with a prioritized list of my child's needs was wonderful. However, just as I hadn't been taught holistic self-care approaches, especially those that pertain to a physically altering experience like giving birth, as I looked at my brown baby boy, I realized that that information would not magically be taught to him either.

From the moment you feel like you are responsible for another life, whatever loose-knit thoughts about self-care you may have had can drift further and further away from you and more towards servicing that little life's needs. Activities you once normally did to maintain your emotional, spiritual, physical and social stability now have to share priority.

The way implement self-care before becoming a mom has everything to do with how you adjust and manage your self-care *after* you become one. Knowing how to assess your needs through self-actualization or outside help becomes more critical when another life is relying on your every decision.

One of the threats to having poor self-care practices is something I call *Mechanical Mommy Syndrome*. This made-up syndrome is the way I viewed successful motherhood -- servicing needs without allowing emotions to derail the process. Even to this day, (my son is almost four years old), to balance a work-home-social schedule while servicing his needs and that of a husband requires me to turn my emotional needs chip off so often, the response becomes automatic. Here are a few signs of my made up term Mechanical Mommy Syndrome:

- Handling daily activities on auto pilot, not taking a moment to acknowledge my heart and soul
- Avoiding any activity or conversation that will stir up emotions that may not obey a timeline
- The literal thought passing through my mind: *I don't have time to feel this right now*
- Gradually skipping activities that may bring sheer and ultimate pleasure (throwing out the baby with the bath water)
- Feeling bad about feeling sad
- Decreasing interest in beautifying myself
- Repeating daily pre-listed scripts for everyone in the house just to get out of the door in the morning and to get my child to bed at night
- Denying occasional deviations from the day-to-day schedule
- Ignoring reoccurring physical aches or pains while playing with my child

The issue with each of these signs is not *that* they occur. The problem with these signs is *how often* they occur – occasionally or frequently. Disconnecting from your feelings is the root cause of disconnecting from what you *need*. Running from difficult or intense emotions is like running from the cheat sheet to your Self Care Plan creation. Critical and intense emotions tell you something about yourself that no person can ever tell you as profoundly as in that moment. As a mother, these intense emotions can color the overall parenting experience. When they are intense, your children feel it.

I remember when I discovered that I had a habit and survival reflex of running from intense emotions. In 2005, I survived a miscarriage. It was my very first time being pregnant and I was so happy. There were pregnancy magazines and nausea candies all over my apartment in downtown Atlanta. I was very much in love with being pregnant.

Four months into the pregnancy, I walked into my first ultrasound appointment. The ultrasound tech brought a black and white screen image up of this little kidney-looking shape that was my first baby. I was smiling so big. She moved the cold slimy Vaseline-like substance around my lower tummy. She pushed a few buttons and said she would be right back. I wondered if it was a girl or a boy. I wondered how big my tummy would get. When she re-entered the room, she said she was trying to reach my doctor. I thought nothing of it because I was nauseous. I told her I needed to get to work soon and was going to leave. She excused herself again and returned shortly with a sad look on her face. I ignored that, too.

When I heard the words, "your baby has no heartbeat" I didn't think that had anything to do with me. I said, "OK, what does that mean?" She replied, "Your baby is not alive. I am so sorry."

I sat in shock, trying to process the news. The ultrasound technician broke down crying. I watched her and watched her some more. Suddenly, I felt a thump in my chest as I thought about having to tell everyone, especially my husband who, at the time, was my fiancée. It took a while for it to hit me that my baby was gone.

The technician snapped me out of my fog somehow long enough to tell me I had to have surgery, which they couldn't schedule for three days. I walked out, nauseous still. I don't remember getting to the car.

I barely remember telling my fiancée. We sat in shock. In that moment, I exhibited my first symptom of Mechanical Mommy Syndrome, which of course was textbook shock, when I told him to drop me off at work. I completely disconnected, wandered into the office and sat at my computer. My first phone call was to my self-care angel and best friend Michelle. As soon as I heard her voice, I began to cry. Through streams of tears I said, "Michelle, I lost the baby." I don't remember her immediate response. I cried more. I asked her, *"What do I do?"*

Michelle asked me where I was. I told her work. She said, "Ok, right now, I want you to book a hotel room and go there immediately. You can't go home--there is baby stuff all over the place." I did what she said. For the next few days, I was a machine. I was walking around, still nauseous. My body felt pregnant, my belly was still prominent, my child's body was still inside me, but the ultrasound tech said the baby's spirit was gone. I don't remember all of those days. I think I went to the doctor. I believe I spoke to people, but I don't remember it. The day of the surgery, I managed to hold it all in until they wheeled me into the operating room. As the anesthesiologist asked me to count backwards, I let out the most vulnerable weep for myself I had ever had and fell deep asleep.

When I woke up, I heard the voice of my mother on the phone, calling from Louisiana. Groggy from the anesthesia, I tried to respond to her. My fiancée helped me get home, where my dear roommate's mother had completely redecorated my room: no baby magazines, no nausea candies. Just me and my most intense feeling ever--loss. If ever I became introduced to Mechanical Mommy Syndrome, it was then. A severe case of grief and shock, yes... but it introduced me to walking around professionally disconnected while continuing to serve others sooner than I was able to heal properly. Katrina hit a few weeks later and the rest of life continued, as did my grief, disconnection emotionally and mechanical mommy syndrome.

Mechanical Mommy was in full effect with no regrets for a very long time, until I saw myself--cranky, disconnected and about to pass out from neglecting myself. The child I did have later, my son deserved a healthier mother. I deserved to be healthier, but when you've earned a PhD in disconnecting, how on earth do you figure out a new way to live?

How is a mother to provide if on the inside she is coiled up in a corner crying all day? Why address intense and painful emotions that could potentially shut you down? No one at work is going to wait for me to leisurely process a painful experience. The grocery store clerk will not call my cell phone and say, "hi ma'am, we heard you were having a tough day and wanted to deliver free groceries to your house, unpack them, then prepare dinner."

Caring for yourself as a mother requires the use of every component of this Self Care Program, as often as possible: checking in with a Self Care Buddy or Support Group, asking advice from your Self Care Dream Team members, finding the time to assess your needs, and creating baby steps. Your quality of life matters, not because you are a mother, but because *you* matter.

I have received some of the best advice and support from other moms. If you do only one self-care act as a new mother, please be sure to socialize with other moms and create a Self Care Support Group for Moms in your area. Here are a few words of advice from my Dream Team Member moms that have carried me:

Self-care for mothers is not a luxury but a necessity to survive the trying years of rearing productive and happy human beings. As mothers, we give so much of ourselves away to others. We must give the same quality time to loving ourselves as we do our children. To not do so is to declare warfare on the spirit.
-- Kottavei, Mother Author of Mentalcourse: Modern Erotic Haiku and Tapestries

Mothers are the heartbeat of the family. The best thing she can ever do for her family is to take care of herself physically, mentally and spiritually.
- Rosalind Goldman, Mother

With so many titles--wife-mom-daughter-friend-employee, it is easy to forget that you are also. You. I lost myself somewhere between balancing our budget and fixing dinner plates. Without the help of the self-care dream team and plan, I would still be sadly waddling in a puddle of breast milk. When I began to take care of myself, I became complete again and more effective at my many titles.

-- -- Charity Jordan, M. Ed.

Self-care can be defined and fulfilled in many ways. I try to incorporate small elements of self-care in everything I do. As a Mom, I focus on the love that my daughter unselfishly shares with me. As a wife I focus on the blessing of sharing the present and planning the future with my husband. When connecting with my best girlfriends, I focus on the balance, strong support, and humor that we so easily share. At work I focus on the role I play in protecting the public from the impacts of weather and climate events. Of course I like to slip away to the spa when I can, but I'm not at a void if I can't. I try to extract self-care from everything that I do.

--Dr. Michelle Hawkins-Aguilar - Mother

Remember to define your own success and not to allow society to dictate it for you. Society tries to press upon me that success should look like (1) a particular car (that I cannot truly afford), (2)a particular type of residence in a particular zip code (that I cannot truly afford nor is truly convenient for me), (3) a particular type of spouse (even at the expense of being unhappy and lonely), (4) a particular type of status/job description (even if it is tiring, inconvenient and leaves me with no disposable time for myself, family or friends). As such, I must resist the capitalist notion to strive to be like others or to always want more. Instead, I am intentional about being content with who I am, who I really want to be and not worry so much on the material or the appearance. Thus, one must define their own notion of success and be content with it and comfortable knowing that your life is your own. Self-care should be based in or include self-acceptance. I think the notion of success should be relative and is indeed situational. You have to know your own self and situation. Women particularly have to struggle with notions of what a good wife, mother, employee are and self-care through self-acceptance helps me to balance it out.

-- Attorney Tawanna Morgan, Founder Ma'at Law Firm and mother

Chapter 7: Self Care in the Work Place

*I have looked in the mirror every morning
and asked myself: 'If today were the last
day of my life, would I want to do what I
am about to do today?' And whenever the
answer has been 'No' for too many days in a
row, I know I need to change something.* --
Steve Jobs

Money is the primary reason why most of us work and, hopefully, your work meets your basic *economic* self-care needs. Of course, there are some people who are financially set and work for other reasons. Even those of us who work for money often want more than a paycheck: Recognition. Purpose. Prestige. Comradery. To make a difference. To be of service.

It is tricky to take care of yourself in a group when you care so much about the overall group mission – family, church, community, work. It is a balancing act between what *you* need and what the *group* or the *community* *needs*. Work is no different. And the politics of the work environment make taking care of yourself even trickier.

Just as the fear of losing your romantic partner may keep you from expressing some of your true feelings, the fear of losing your job may keep you from taking care of your personal needs in the context of work. However, it is still important to ensure that your *core* self-care needs are being met if you plan on contributing your best work.

Do you know what your core self-care needs are for work? Which of these apply to you?

- ☐ I need to feel appreciated.
- ☐ I need to be paid fairly.
- ☐ I need to be heard and respected.
- ☐ I need to be guided.
- ☐ I need to part of a team that I respect.
- ☐ I need to learn more about my profession.
- ☐ I need a clear career path.
- ☐ I need to constantly learn new things.
- ☐ I need to make a difference.
- ☐ I need an opportunity to make more money.
- ☐ I need acknowledgement.

☐ I need to enjoy what I do.

☐ I need to be inspired by my work or my co-workers.

☐ I need a friendly, family-like work environment.

☐ I need to express myself creatively.

☐ I need _____. (fill in the blank)

Now go back through this list and mark which of the needs you selected that are actually being met by your work. Are the results what you expected? Or are you surprised? If your needs are not being met, what can you do? Get started on your Self Care Plan for work.

Here are a couple of scenarios that may help you think of ways in which you can exercise self-care in the workplace. Every workplace is different so protect the paycheck, maintain your quality of work while working your Self Care Plan.

Scenario 1 – Manager Woes

Your manager is always late for your weekly one-on-one meeting. She barely apologizes and proceeds to talk about personal things, nothing work-related. It is hard not to take her chronic lateness personally and while you don't mind the "girlfriend sessions" sometimes, you'd rather these meetings be used as they're supposed to: to discuss critical or priority issues you have regarding your projects. How can you take care of yourself in this scenario?

- Prepare for the meeting. Outline what you would like to walk away with after the meeting.
- Have a hardcopy of your list of needs in hand during the meeting.
- Speak up about the specific information you need during the meeting.
- Send a follow up email once the meeting is completed confirming what was discussed and listing any outstanding issues needing to be address in the next meeting.

Often, when we have needs in the workplace that haven't been met, there are actions we can take to better address those needs. The need to feel appreciated, be paid fairly, be given an opportunity to make more money or to be heard will require you to adopt new habits around communicating and documenting your own activities on the job above what may be expected of you. This is excellent self-care in the workplace because you have complete control over how you manage yourself in any and all circumstances. The other benefit is that healthy self-care behavior in one workplace translates well to another one. You are practicing self-management tools that you can take with you, no matter where you are working.

Self-care in the workplace can feel overwhelming when your work product is dependent upon others in the same office who may or may not be pulling their weight. Just as in the previous example, documenting your work activity and noting *lessons learned* once a project is completed is essential to your self-care in the workplace. Without documenting your lessons learned, your hard work is available for everyone else on the team. When you document your accomplishments, procedures and lessons learned, you are able to review for yourself where you need to set boundaries as opposed to sharing a random feeling of frustration in a meeting.

Typically when we are pulling the weight of others repeatedly, it is to the detriment of something on our plate: whether we lose losing personal time with friends and family or see of our own work suffer, we are paying for someone else's lack of activity out of our own life pockets. This is not a sustainable situation if we are truly taking care of ourselves.

A Self Care Plan in the workplace is the same as at home. It will challenge your need for (or acceptance of) things that are not helping you live your life's purpose like:

- The need to be right and in control all the time
- The need to carry the weight of those who consciously don't want to carry their own
- The need to feel secure and safe around things you already know vs. doing a good job while exploring the new frontier of your own career

The bottom line is to begin your Self-Care Plan in the workplace today. Use your *Self Care Matters Journal & Playbook* daily. Consider forming a Self Care Support Group after work hours. Use the following self-care mantra and movement sequence created by the Self Care Agency at your desk each time you feel distanced from your self-care goals:

As you say...	Do this movement...
I nourish myself.	Place your finger tips on your navel.
I do my best.	Place your finger tips on the center of your chest.
I say "thank you."	Place your fingertips at the center of your throat
...and I release the	Place your finger tips on your forehead, then gently release them, floating your hands down.

Nothing is really work unless you would rather be doing something else.
—J.M. Barrie

Chapter 8: Becoming a Self Care Activist

In our struggle to dismantle systems of oppression, we are morally obligated to fight and organize as hard and as long as we possibly can. Self-care allows us to meet that moral obligation by living longer and stronger!

-Activist Attorney Mawuli Mel Davis

Activists not only protest but they plan, organize and request help in addressing particular wrongs. There is always a culprit or source of the injustice. The source may be a specific person, business or organization that has done an injustice to those not strong or informed enough to resist.

A child abuse advocate dedicated to her or his cause may lose sleep brainstorming ways to help free a child from an abusive environment. An education activist might forego a good football game if his mentee needs him to help him study for a math test. There are many quiet activists out there who, disgusted by the condition our society is in, have chosen to join an organization or do something in their own, unpublicized way.

So, what if the culprit is *not* a person, business or institution? What if the culprit is a set of circumstances: missed education, lack of love, a traumatic experience and low self-esteem? Who will be the activist fighting that fight? Who will look at this severe need then choose to ask for guidance? Create a Self Care Plan while increasing awareness around the issue they care about? The Self Care activist. An activist is also a community member who sometimes needs help.

Activists tend to find comfort in helping others while dodging the need to address their own critical self-care needs. Helping others soothes them and feeds their need to fulfill their purpose. Unfortunately, there are limits to how many and how often you can help when you are crippled by your own boundaries. It's time for that to stop.

If you are struggling with any kind of self-care challenge, as an activist, the fight you are dodging is one that will make a major impact on your ability to help others. It is the fight against the part of you that is avoiding your own self-care needs.

You can fight for others and yourself.

I see change agents, do gooders, leaders, brave soldiers and activists fighting injustices everyday who won't fight for themselves in certain areas of their own lives. These same activists fight the good fight against serious issues like genocide, environmental discrimination, self-hatred, human trafficking and corporate bullying, but shy away from the fight for their own mental, physical, social or financial health challenges.

Who will fight for your cause when your self-care habits hit rock bottom? How can those you want to help see an example of true freedom in you if you have a self-care need consistently going unaddressed? Show them that your life matters too by taking care of that life. Show them that their life matters by showing them that your life matters. When we truly are free and caring for ourselves spiritually/emotionally, economically, artistically, physically, educationally and socially, our purpose for being here and helping others magnifies beyond our comprehension.

Plan to care for yourself holistically while fighting for your community and watch things change.

As a Self-Care Activist in your own life, develop a Self Care Plan based on your own personal needs. Picture this: an activist for abused children who has a self-care lifestyle that guarantees that he will be a voice for the voiceless and instigate change wherever the battle takes him. Because he worked the Self Care Plan and healed his economic wounds, when it's time to travel, he can afford it. When it's time to exhibit healthy self-care habits to community members just learning how to take care of themselves, he activist can model it. Imagine a college student, the first in her family to attain a degree, being her own self-care activist as she pioneers a life of social justice, activism and self-care. That is showing the ultimate gratitude to her family.

As a community activist taking care of yourself contributes to saving what's good in the world.

Humility and self-care can exist together. In fact, maintaining a Self Care Plan requires you to consistently remain humble to that which you don't know how to do alone. The bravest action you could take is to **not** allow your fear to stop you from establishing a secure foundation for your own wellbeing while helping others. If you are drowning in an area of self-care, save yourself and become your own activist so you can be available to help save others.

Unfortunately, we often don't know we are spiritually/emotionally, economically, artistically, physically, educationally or socially drowning until it's too late. Don't give up on yourself. Be brave and adapt a self-care lifestyle so you can continue to be present and to be what's good in this world.

> *To face the realities of our lives is not a reason for despair—despair is a tool of your enemies. Facing the realities of our lives gives us motivation for action. For you are not powerless... You know why the hard questions must be asked. It is not altruism, it is self-preservation—survival.*
> - Audre Lorde in Oberlin College Commencement Address, 1989

Grief and Activism

My work in supporting individuals and families through the Davis Bozeman Law Firm exposed me to many stories of grief and activism. Mothers and fathers whose children or other family members have been killed as a result of preventable violence carry a heavy burden of grief. That weight and stress sometimes transfers to our staff and community activists who are bombarded with grief and struggle every day, effecting them greatly.

Through the Davis Bozeman Law Firm, attorneys, therapists, community partners and community activists work together to support the needs of grieving clients to the best of their ability. But, our clients' journey through grief can truly only be walked alone. Moving through the commonly recognized stages of grief (denial, isolation, anger, bargaining and acceptance) is different for everyone and can take years.

While many parents and family members, like the family of Nicholas Thomas, manage to translate a tragedy into an educational format to help others while dealing with their own grief, the activism who is born out of grief should incorporate a Self Care Plan.

Trauma, tragedy and grief can zap your memory, your will power and your belief in anything being worthwhile. Prayer, counseling and an active Self Care Plan are all tools that social workers, community service based workers, attorneys, therapists and those deeply affected grief can use to find a way to stay afloat then heal.

Allow the Self Care Plan described in this book to be one option to support your selfless activism or grief-laced journey. Justice is healing. Fighting for justice is healing. Being a part of the bigger battle for justice may help to channel the sense of hopelessness towards fighting to better protect someone else. Implementing a Self Care Plan can help you take care of yourself while continuing your purpose. Find a support group and use the 7 Self Care Keys. Allow the activist in you to fight for your own emotional and spiritual self-care so that you can continue to fight for justice for the ones you love.

Chapter 9: Are You a Self Care Revolutionary?

*When we speak we are afraid our words
will not be heard or welcomed. But when we
are silent, we are still afraid. So it is better
to speak.*

-- Audre Lorde

On my freshman journey to Howard University, my father told me, *"Anana, I know you are my introspective passionate child who believes in fighting for the creation of this utopian village where everyone is kind, sings, dances and eats all day. But when you see the struggle in the path to helping those less fortunate, don't end up on a corner eating bean pies with incense burning and yapping about the ills of the world or what could have been all day. There are enough martyrs. We don't need any more martyrs. Do your work. Make a difference and then keep doing your work."*

This was one of my first adult lessons in self-care. It was hard to see suffering and still have Calculus III homework to do as an engineering student. It was difficult to juxtapose an economically depressed community in Washington, DC alongside a higher education institution like Howard University. When a young freshman dangled her legs over the edge of her room window because she wanted to commit suicide in Frazier Hall, I wanted to immediately create a sister circle support group in the dorms on the Harriet Tubman quad.

Revolutionary: radically new or
innovative; outside or beyond established
procedure, principles, etc. --dictionary.com

My father knew me oh so well. I cared so much about those who were struggling that it took me until now to really understand his words. He wanted me to take care of myself while still feeling true compassion for my community. I tried my best to do that and lost the battle many times. Whether it was for family, friends or a child in the community, I consistently sacrificed my own self care needs for those of a cause or the needs of a friend.

Now, as a Self Care Revolutionary, I choose to humble myself to the strong pull of diversions, distractions and desires to help others long enough to implement a program that helps me take care of myself while still caring for my community. Now I can control my decisions by balancing what I truly *need* with what I truly *want*. I need to be healthy and to check in with myself spiritually, emotionally, economically, physically, educationally and socially to be a self-care revolutionary committed to the community.

To be a revolutionary, you must be inspired. I am inspired by children who are growing up in conditions I could never imagine yet who still carry a sense of compassion in their hearts. I see the child in the eyes of the adult who never recovered from an early trauma and I want to help. I am inspired by my father, who admitted he often didn't have all the answers while raising us but still shared what he knew to be true with his children. My father taught me to be grateful every day and to never forget that there are those who don't come close to having my blessings. I pray for those people, and, through my community work, I share what knowledge, skills and talents I have in hopes of helping them.

*If you have never found something so
dear and precious to you that you will
die for it, then you are not fit to live. You
are afraid that you will be criticized by
others. You are afraid that you will lose
your popularity, or you are afraid that
somebody will stab you, or shoot at you,
or bomb your house. So you refuse to
take a stand. Well you may go on and
live to be 90 years old, but you are
already dead. You died when you
refused to stand up for right. You died
when you refused to stand up for truth.
You died when you refused to stand up
for justice. Don't ever think that you are
by yourself. Go to jail if necessary, but
you never go alone. Take a stand for
that which you know is right. The world
might misunderstand you and criticize
you, but you are never alone. One with
God is the majority* -- Martin Luther
King, Jr.

A Self-Care Revolutionary is constantly bombarded by
reasons not to take care of herself, attacked by familiar,

self-sabotaging habits, and surrounded by rules that don't support you taking care of yourself. But we fight to take care of ourselves anyway.

It's not enough to be an activist just for others, you must also be a self-care revolutionary for yourself. As a community activist, I am committed to contributing to a revolution that helps people heal and feel empowered to heal themselves, to help create the balance of caring for ourselves so that we can better care for others. This is the challenge of a true Self-Care Revolutionary.

Chapter 10: Self Care Buddy System

A Self Care Buddy is a current or former participant in a Self Care Support Group who agrees to accompany you in your self-care journey in a prescribed way: he or she will contact you on a regular basis, in any manner (in person, by phone, email or text) with a simple question -- *How is your self-care going?* A Self Care Buddy is your personal cheerleader, committed to providing you encouragement to help you stay on your Self Care journey and work your plan.

A Self Care Buddy holds a unique position in your life. She may not be a close relative or even a friend that you speak to daily. She will come to know some of your specific challenges and the status of your Self Care development. How does she get to know this? Because you will share this information.

A Buddy can but isn't obligated to share his experiences with you. But he genuinely cares about how you are doing. He knows the value of having a buddy on a journey towards good self-care. He will say things like:

How does it feel to ask for guidance from your Self Care Dream Team members?

Can you think of any baby steps you might take in that self-care category?

Good job on taking care of yourself today.

How can I support you in making that baby step?

Self Care Buddy Interventions

Self Care Buddy interventions happen when a buddy offers and you allow him or her to assist you in performing a self-care step, big or small. The difference between a regular friend helping you accomplish your goal and a Self Care Buddy assisting is that your Self Care Buddy is willing to revisit the step as often as possible until it is accomplished.

Caution: Don't rely on your Self Care Buddy's feedback to guide you. His job is not to advise. Instead he is dedicated to supporting you, listening to you, and encouraging you.

How to Pick a Self Care Buddy

- Ask group leader for recommendation
- Pick somebody you trust and respect
- Put it out there in a Self Care Support Group
- You may have more than one

My Self Care Buddy Intervention Story

I was 19 years old and in need of a root canal after an old filling from my youth finally cracked. In an emergency, I went to see a very old dentist who just so happened to be training a new dentist in the procedure.

Instead of giving me antibiotics to kill the infection first, the lead dentist decided to begin performing the root canal right away. The pain medicine wore off after a few minutes but the dentist decided to continue through my tears. He would occasionally drop some pain killers directly on the tooth, but that didn't help. I cried and repeatedly asked him to stop. Not until the new dentist spoke up, asking him to stop because of the pain I was in did the procedure end. As a result of that traumatic experience, I have held a powerful phobia of dentists and dental procedure. In fact, one of my greatest self-care challenges remains going to the dentist.

One day recently, after having gotten a dental assessment and living on a 24-hour pain killer, I yielded and called my new dentist, Dr. Khalil Cumberbatch, who happens to be one of my Physical Dream Team Members.

During my first visit, he listened to all of my medical fear-related stories, from my first horrible dental experience to my son's birth experience. He listened and responded with sheer and total compliance to addressing my needs and acknowledging my emotions. The experience was amazing. Yet, even though that is true, old fears won out and I failed to make my follow up appointment. The result: an old dental issue reared its ugly head and forced me back into Dr. Cumberbatch's chair. He said I needed a root canal. I wanted to pass out.

I procrastinated for two more weeks until one day my Self Care Buddy and husband, Derrick Parris, said, "I just spoke with your Self Care Dream Team member who tried to call you but you didn't answer. The two of us would to talk to you if that's OK with you."

I twisted my body like a twelve-year-old and said *yes*. My Self Care Buddy husband and Dream Team Member dentist proceeded to encourage and cheerlead me into agreeing to set a final appointment, which I finally did.

In the past, before the Self Care Plan, I would have been embarrassed to tell this story. However, I have learned that some goals in your life will only be reached when compassionate help is provided. Then, prayerfully, and over time, your courage, strength and trust will grow as strong as your Self Care Buddy's and Dream Team member's belief in you. I am grateful my Self Care Buddy and Dream Team member honored my needs, cared about my health, didn't judge me and provided the support I needed to gain the will to take better care of myself.

We may label and place boundaries on things in nature because of their position or action; its biology or chemistry or physical make up. Or if something has a deleterious effect on a specific part of the body.

But, it is important to remember that life has no boundaries. Evidence of ill health in one part of the body may well be a reflection of ill health in another. The oral region can be looked at as a window into the body, and also a conduit. The bacteria we label as being 'oral bacteria' do not see those boundaries that we impose on it. They can and will if the opportunity arises, inhabit other parts of the body as well. A healthy mouth can literally add years to your life. --
Dr. Khalil Cumberpatch, D.D.S.

Chapter 11: How to Start a Self Care Support Group™

After I created the Self Care Program, I decided to start hosting Self Care Support Groups that would allow me and other Self Care participants to check-in regarding overall self-care. I realized I needed to be able to get encouragement on my specific self-care baby steps so I could be accountable to all of what I needed help on. Not surprisingly, several Self Care Program participants found the support groups useful and expressed interest in starting their own groups. Here are a few tips for starting a Self Care Support Group.

- Self Care Support Groups are non-religious gatherings that welcome all to check in, express self-care goals and listen to and support others.
- In order to maintain the integrity and consistency of all Self Care support groups, it is critical that all rules and parameters listed in the most current version of this book be followed. Self Care Support Groups are not designed to replace or serve as counseling sessions.

- Self-care is an intimate act and each Self Care Ambassador assigned to host a support group is responsible for maintaining a safe space in which participants can share. The groups should be held in safe environments and cannot include any device that can record what is discussed.

Why Start a Support Group?

Starting a Self Care Support Group is a wonderful way to ensure you will be surrounded by individuals working the same formatted Self Care Plan as you. Many times a large group of people may all want to get in shape yet go about getting in shape in very different ways. Some ask for guidance and some do not. Without guidance from those with the wisdom to make your self-care journey less aggressive, a person can lose momentum and faith in the process of pushing through to taking better care of them self. Starting a Self Care Support Group allows you to speak the same language with those who want holistic growth in more than one area of their lives along your self-care journey.

Getting Started

To start your own Self Care Matters Support Group™ you only need four things:

- this book
- the Self Care Journal and Playbook | check online for Self Care Check In Form
- a spirit of compassionate leadership
- completion of the Self Care Ambassador Training hosted by the Self Care Agency

Guidelines

Follow these guidelines to start a Self Care Support Group and facilitate the sessions.

1. Each group must have a Certified Self Care Ambassador to coordinate the establishment and maintain the integrity of the group which is established exclusively by the Self Care Agency. Contact the Self Care Agency through our website at www.selfcareagency.com and request a Self Care Support Group Ambassador

Training & Registration Form. Complete the form and submit it through our website upload option.

2. Secure, if possible a co-facilitator/Self Care Ambassador to share the leadership responsibilities.

3. Decide whether your group will be private (by invitation) or open to the general public.

4. Determine how often your group will meet.

5. Each participant needs copy of the Self Care Matters A Revolutionary Approach and the Self Care Matters Journal & Playbook

To Ensure Privacy

To protect the privacy of participants in Self Care Support Groups, please ensure that:

6. No recording or sharing outside of the group.

7. No media of any kind are allowed in for the purpose of utilizing or sharing what is shared in the group meeting.

8. No texting, phone calls, tweeting during group

Standard Agenda

A typical Self Care Support Group meeting runs for 60 to 90 minutes and follows an agenda like this:

- (*Optional*) 30 minutes of free movement or music
- Welcome by facilitator/ Self Care Ambassador
- Reading of the Purpose/ Framework and Guidelines for the Group
- Welcome new members and explain the Self Care Plan components
- Group reads aloud the *7 Self Care Keys*
- Individual Self-Care Check Ins
- Voluntary Self Care Story Sharing
- Closing Group Self Care Affirmation "I nourish myself, do my best, say thank you and release the rest."

The items on the agenda are described below.

Welcome

Follow the ideas here to welcome the support group participants, both returning members and the new visitors.

You may want to ask the group what they know about Self Care and how they heard about the group.

A Self Care Support Group is a safe, warm, welcome environment that allows each participant to listen to or share self-care goals in the categories of spiritual/emotional, economic, physical artistic, educational and social self-care. There is no obligation other than to be courteous to others who are doing their self-care-check-ins and to acquire the two key materials that help you begin creating and implementing your own Self Care Plan.

Purpose

You will want to explain the purpose of the group at each session, especially when there are newcomers.

The purpose of the Self Care Support Group is to gather those interested in getting and giving support so we can all stay committed to our own self-care journey.

This support group is a socially-based, protected meet up for individuals who are courageously voicing their own self-care journeys and are willing to listen to others' self-care goals, setbacks, and successes. It is not a substitute for professional counseling.

If you are feeling the desire to hurt yourself or you are facing a crisis, please contact a professional counselor who can help you face, navigate and heal beyond this moment in your life.

Note: It is important to insist that participants agree NOT to record the session in any way and NOT to share what goes on in the session with anyone who was not a participant.

Explaining the Self Care Plan

Here is an example of a way to explain the Self Care Plan:

How many of you know about the Self Care Plan? For those of you who don't know, the Self Care Plan is an active plan customized by you to write down, track and address your specific spiritual, emotional, economic, artistic, physical, educational and social self-care needs. It is based on the Self Care Matters: A Revolutionary Approach book and the partnering Journal & Playbook, which provides definitions, self-care checklists, activities and challenges for each of you to bravely attempt, if you choose. The Journal & Playbook is also a space for you to store information on your Dream Team members, baby step goals, Self Care Buddy contact information and a Self Care in the Workplace action plan. You'll learn more about all this as we go.

Self Care Check In

Here is an idea for facilitating the Self Care Check In:

We have time to hear updates and goals everyone has set forth to take better care of themselves. Please limit your sharing to no more than one category per person. No one in the group will offer advice, a product or service during the group session.

Self Care Story Sharing

In each meeting, the facilitator will open the floor for participants to share a challenge he or she has recently experienced in setting or meeting a self-care goal. (As facilitator, you may find that it helps for you to start the story sharing session.)

Explain that this session is for sharing, not critiquing or providing advice. All suggestions, feedback, and comments should be saved until after the group session has completed. Do encourage participant to add comments and share their own stories. Speaking up is a form of self-care.

Group Affirmation

Because our bodies, minds and souls are connected, it helps tremendously to acknowledge all three aspects of ourselves when our self-care regimen is in need. I taught this simple self-care affirmation movement sequence that I had been using to personally ground myself when I felt lost or at a self-care rock bottom. We now incorporate these affirmations into the support group session:

I took good care of myself by coming here today. I matter to me each and every day. When my heart is heavy and I feel sadness in my chest, I repeat this self-care goal so my dreams can manifest:

I nourish myself, do my best, say thank you and release the rest. I nourish myself, do my best, say thank you and release the rest. I nourish myself, do my best, say thank you and release the rest.

There are specific movements that accompany this mantra:

As you say...   Do this movement...

I nourish myself.	Place your fingertips at your navel.
I do my best.	Place your fingertips at the center of your chest.
I say "thank you."	Place your fingertips at the center of your throat
...and I release the	Place your finger tips on your forehead, then gently release them, floating your hands down, palms open.

Repeat the sequence three times speaking out loud, then three times whispering, then one time silently thinking the words while doing the motions.

To give you an idea of how effective these affirmations can be, in 2011, Saniyyah Griffin, then General Manager of the Carol's Daughter store in Lenox Mall in Atlanta, hosted our very first Self Care Day celebration in partnership with AfriSalsa and A Lotus Legacy. We had self-care stations for hair, healthy movement and guidance for recovering from past traumas. We had participants recite the group affirmations. A 911 operator who attended that event sent this feedback:

> *Last night an apartment building housing 30 units caught on fire. When my officers got there, young women were jumping from the balconies [because] they could not safely get out of their apartment doors. I had just taught my partner the "mantra" Wednesday night [that I learned at the Self Care Day workshops] ... I said the Lord's prayer and then the mantra --this calmed me down and allowed me to get my officers and the citizens the help they needed. I'm not sure a week ago I could have handled it with as much finesse as I did early this morning. Thank you."*

Reciting these affirmations is a powerful exercise in self-love. Encourage support group participants to practice these affirmations on their own. You may want to provide a paper copy for each participant.

Closing the Session

End the session by thanking participants for coming and for taking good care of themselves. Encourage them to continue to build their Dream Team Members and to find and keep in touch with their Self Care Buddies. Recommend that every member download the free Self Care Matters app which helps them check in with each other in between meetings and describes the framework of the Self Care Program.

How to Prepare to Facilitate a Support Group

1. Review the information found in this chapter.
2. Visit the website monthly for updates and complimentary Self Care Agency forms and other tools provided.
3. Contact the Self Care Agency online with any questions.

Be sure to have the following tools available for each support group session:

- Music (*optional*)

- Self Care Matter Journal & Playbooks (for sale)
- Self Care Check in Handouts (copies available)
- Guidelines (for your reference)
- Closing Affirmation (for your reference and to hand out)

Chapter 12: Self Care Rock Bottom

The beauty of adversity is that when we hit bottom, the only way to go is up.
—Dana Arcuri, Reinventing You: Simple Steps to Transform Your Body, Mind, & Spirit

Self Care *Rock Bottom* is the complete absence of the desire to take care of yourself holistically or categorically. We can remain in denial about how low our interest is in taking care of ourselves, but there are certain actions that trigger a red flag that we must honor. For example, if you skipped every other chapter in this book and came straight to this one, you should call someone immediately and ask for help and guidance. Skipping to this chapter is a sign you need to welcome the love and support of others to help inspire you to take better care of yourself.

If you are even *questioning* whether or not you've hit a Self Care Rock bottom, please ask for help. Visit the SelfCareDay.com website for emergency numbers for organizations and institutions set up to help you take care of yourself emotionally, artistically, physically, economically, educationally and socially.

Rock bottom means it is time to borrow someone else's belief in us until we believe in ourselves again.

When my son was learning to walk, he was really afraid of falling. Like most children, he would wobble a bit, and then give up. I'd sit back watching and waiting for him to find the courage on his own and, like any first time mom, would worry that he would never find it. I would watch him like a television show, distant from his process of learning. Then I tried something. I held my hand out a little further than he was reaching and said, "come on Z you can do it." He immediately went for my hand over and over again until he built up his confidence to walk on his own.

Let someone hold a hand out for you, then walk in faith. You don't have to understand or know how it will work out, you just have to see a hand extended and keep walking, one foot at a time, one day at a time.

Rock bottom is a terrifying place that absolutely requires an extended hand to survive it. It requires someone to help you rebuild that self-care muscle. You will need help exercising the desire to do activities that take care of you spiritually/emotionally, economically, artistically, physically, educationally or socially.

There will be moments when you are watching yourself, almost in an out-of-body experience, actually doing something you thought was terrifying and impossible. Your actions may say you are confident and faith-driven, but your heart may be drowning in worry and fear. Keep walking anyway. Allow your Self Care Dream Team member, in whatever category critical for you, to extend a hand.

There is help out there. Trained professionals in the area of counseling have heard it all. Don't be ashamed of where you are. Call them, reach out to the hotlines. In addition to psychologists and crisis intervention facilities, there are other services that can help give you some relief. For example, there is a phenomenal sister in Atlanta who is trained and certified in massage therapy who created the service and brand, Mental Vacation™ . She takes you at your self-care rock bottom and not only massages you but she incorporates customized encouraging affirmations with other layered techniques to nurture and care for you during a rock bottom moment.

If you've hit a financial rock bottom for whatever reason, ignore the embarrassment and shame long enough to take a self-care step and make the first call to an accountant, a financial consultant or a financially savvy friend. Add this person to your Economic Dream Team once they have agreed to help you. Continue establishing your Self Care Plan, because rock bottom in one area can have a negative impact on another area.

The Self Care Plan you develop by yourself, with a buddy, a mentor, a partner or a group is your personal, customized reference tool for growing and healing in your life. Having a Self Care Plan actually written down helps you remember what to do when the pain or confusion of a low moment in your life makes you temporarily forget how to care for yourself. The plan is flexible because you create it based on where you are. When you hit rock bottom, you may realize that you require a *new* plan. Find the courage to create a new Self Care Plan.

Quietly agonizing over difficult challenges, past traumas and fears of the future is probably not the most effective route to self-care. On the other hand, writing down what you need, who may be able to help and where you can go to be encouraged, means you have a plan that you can use, that can give you some control.

The pain probably won't disappear overnight, but you'll have a gentler, more caring journey getting back up.

Appendices

Creating Your Own Self Care Strategy

When we decide to dedicate our lives to growing a business, we develop a strategy and a plan. No matter how loose or subconscious the strategy, one is created and adjusted to meet the goal of having a business. A business that wants to stay open and flourish will find a way to be flexible and keep very specific frameworks in place which include address the critical needs of the business. It is a strategy to review the needs and recognize moments when the needs a not getting met. Creating a Self Care Strategy to compliment your overall Self Care Plan is really about regular assessment of changing needs in a strategic way. For instance, a foody that does not include food in their personal Self Care Strategy is not being strategic and realistic.

If you are truly ready to develop your own Self Care Strategy, here is what you need to repeat on a regular basis.

- Ask yourself *regularly* the following,

  [BLOCK]   Do I Have a Block?

[LOOP]   Am I Stuck in a Loop?

[PLAN]   Am I Sticking to My Self Care Plan?

- Only speak about your critical self-care needs with those who are supportive.
- Participation not Perfection is the Strategy.
- Make your Self Care Strategy & Plan VISIBLE.

For this to be a strategic move customized for you, put these words 'BLOCK LOOP PLAN' somewhere visible to YOU. Hang it by your mirror in a frequently used bathroom with a list of your Self Care Goals nearby. Schedule this list of questions to pop up on your calendar once a week. This is a strategy customized for you. What do YOU need to continue *paying attention* to your Self Care Goals and Plan?

Emotional Slavery Exists.

Emotional slavery exists. The more commonly understood institution of slavery on American soil was kept alive by feeding off of the lives of many families and communities for hundreds of years. To end that system meant completely stopping the livelihood of the millions who were profiting generationally from slavery. Emotional slavery, although it can be cleverly masked and hidden, exists and is fueling this present day economy.

The most broken and beaten individuals in the most disadvantaged communities were only taught to survive not how to take care of themselves. Low self-care choices made out of desperation, a lack of resources, guidance and support layered on top of a racist environment is the breeding ground for feeling shame and embarrassment. As a result, the broken and ignored become even more broken in spirit, ridiculed and ultimately dead or in jail. Feeling trapped by embarrassment and shame so much so that you do not take care of yourself and make healthy self-care choices is a form of emotional slavery. Not only is emotional slavery common place, it is also difficult to free yourself from. It is difficult to see that you are emotionally enslaved when so many are also enslaved emotionally around you. It is difficult to change who you spend time with if those people use your shame and embarrassment as a tool to help benefit their own cause.

There are thousands of successful people who have failed or made a mistake and kept trying again without letting shame or embarrassment stop them. Yet, when those from disadvantaged communities make a mistake, it can do more than just teach them a lesson. Those mistakes can cause a build up of shame that can paralyze them. Those mistakes could even cost them their lives. Creating a Self Care Plan and a strategy is how you free yourself, no matter where you live, who raised you or what resources are around you. The journey to freedom will not be easy. You have find the courage to search out and ask for help and not let shame or embarrassment stop you. This journey can be hard because you have developed habits and relationships based on low self-care behavior *and* changing your self-care behavior means disrupting the money making systems built on your sadness, embarrassment, shame, low self-care habits and pain. Those systems will not go down without a fight.

Because of this, working on your Self Care Plan will always feel a challenging and uncomfortable in the beginning. It will take courage to start and continue your plan. The entrapment you feel in the area you require better care in can go away quickly with every Self Care Baby Step you take. The question is not, can you take a self-care step, it is how will you handle the unkind, uncomfortable path to freedom interrupted regularly by those benefiting off of your poor self-care choices and emotional imprisonment. You will create a plan and implement your strategy, that's how. Enacting of self-care on a daily basis is what freedom from emotional slavery feels like.

Enacting of self-care on a daily basis is what freedom from emotional slavery feels like.

Do this, scan the categories of care outlined in this book [S.E.A.P.E.S.]. If your stomach feels like a knot, or you feel a tense nervousness when passing your eyes over a particular category, that is a category you need freedom in. Do not avoid it. Ask for help now. Create a Self Care

Baby Step now. The goal of taking care of yourself is not to reach every goal immediately, but to create a pattern of behavior that frees you from feeling afraid to try to take care of yourself. Life can sucker punch you out of nowhere completely turning your normal needs upside down.

When that happens you may not know exactly what to do, but you will have a Self Care Plan and a strategy to find what you need then go after it. *That... is... freedom.* No man, woman or child should keep you from feeling free to take care of yourself. Anytime you do not feel free, emotionally free to take care for yourself, you are consciously experiencing a form of emotional slavery.

Being afraid to take care of yourself is accepted because in this society, feeling afraid to take care of yourself is normalized and capitalized on. As a result, many hide out of embarrassment the critical state they are living in spiritually, emotionally, economically, artistically, physically, educationally and or socially and do not take aggressive moves to address those needs. Our environment can easy reinforce emotional slavery or we can drench our homes, cars and workplace environments with revolutionary self-care tools that keep us focused on our priority needs. This is how we battle the many barriers created to stop us from taking care of ourselves.

You battle is against the strong belief that surviving is enough. Only few choose to fight the battle of wanting to do more than just survive and even fewer tell their self-care story of winning. The story of fighting through shame and embarrassment to do more than just survive.

Surviving is not gentle. Surviving is not kind. Surviving is surviving. It is a brutal process of day to day scrounging for a way to satisfy basic needs while fighting to not show how hard it just surviving is on your face. Just surviving is spirit breaking and hope stealing.

Caring for oneself, ones family and community is doing more than surviving. It is freedom. Freedom to address critical self-care needs of pleasing others. Free to push through a Self Care Block of fear, embarrassment or shame and take self-care baby step every single day. Free to know how to break an A.F.D. Loop so you don't spend your life complaining about the same thing over and over again. Freedom is having a Self Care Strategy and a Plan laid out, visible and hanging on your wall so you cannot lose focus.

Understand, you will feel free with each critical self-care decision you make. For each category of care you address, the people in your world who want to stay, will need to adjust in some small or big way for that freedom you have found to sustain itself. Sustaining your freedom from never going back to emotional slavery is about keeping your Self Care Strategy in play at all times. Check in with yourself and ask, "Am I blocked, am I stuck in a loop and am I sticking to my plan?" Join a Self Care Matters Support Group.

You must strengthening your self-care muscle with daily acts of self-care to be able to respond to all the sucker punches life throws your way. A revolutionary's approach to self-care is one focused on freedom from emotional slavery.

The Underground Railroad is famously known for being a path to freedom for many enslaved Africans. What some, other than researchers of that time, do *not* know is there were intricate puzzle-like components of that path which made the Underground Railroad possible. Of the many brave and powerful people who contributed to the path of freedom for millions from the South to the North, there were a collection of quilters along this vast route who hid secret messages in the pattern designs of quilts they designed and hung in their windows. These quilts helped guide slaves from state to state, home to home, cramped basement crawl spaces to crawl spaces and cave to cave until they reached freedom. This select group of creative revolutionary artists were among the Underground Railroad Quilters Code. Cultural artists have always been some of the most important revolutionaries in our movements addressing our pain and covering in the arts us as a moment of safety.

When you decide to free yourself from emotional slavery, you must find the states, cities, homes, programs, organizations, businesses and cave-like events that hang a proverbial creatively coded quilt in the window for you to recognize it is a safe place to practice self-care. Find those people and places that are safe for you to feel emotionally free to make a mistake and care for yourself. You must understand that the popular society thinks emotional slavery either doesn't exist or is normal and acceptable. Everyone walks around like it is normal because pain, sadness, fear and shame keep people accepting relationships, products and jobs that also perpetuate feelings of shame and embarrassment. A manager using fear to keep you in line on a job instead of helping your career to flourish so the business can flourish as well is implementing a form of emotional slavery. You can work there during the day, and work to free yourself with a Self Care Plan at night.

Shame and embarrassment are powerful whips to carry and some who have been programmed to accept this way of controlling others as normal will take the opportunity to control another person in that way. You run into 'emotional overseers' every day as they dangle the whip of embarrassment over your head to silence you and paralyze you. It is important that you snatch that whip out of their hand one Self Care Baby Step at a time. One day, you will grow tired of being afraid of being embarrassed about not accomplishing a goal because your exhaustion with being broke, starved of affection or isolated from happiness will shatter your world. On that day, take a Self Care Baby Step, then rest. Take another one, then rest.

Allow those who understand your path to emotional freedom and self-care to offer you cover for the moment, for the night. Allow you Self Care Dream Team Member to point you in the direction of the next self-care station until you start to be able read the code in the quilts yourself.

Like the many maroons around the world who fought for their freedom then created a space for themselves in the same harsh environments, you will adapt. Your environment will begin to change because you will change it to meet your critical needs. If you need a peaceful moment in your own home, you can create that. If you need support from those who care about the same things you care about, you can have that.

Your journey to face any Self Care Blocks, recognize then break tunnel and A.F.D. Loops or remove yourself from people who do *not* support your critical self-care needs may feel like a brutal obstacle course. However brutal it may feel, you will get stronger with each obstacle. You will feel more comfortable with making critical self-care based decisions and saying 'no' when it matters. Get comfortable with taking care of your critical needs *first* so you can soften the blow of the journey and change the difficulty rating of each obstacle by getting emotionally stronger one day at a time. Critical self-care needs *not* addressed make any and every part of your journey through life a more grueling and difficult one.

So, as you push forward from this text and revisit the chapters that are most helpful then share in discussions with friends and family, remember to *never* accept emotional slavery for your life. No matter how murky the waters are as you step forward, please keep taking your Self Care Baby Steps one moment at a time. Emotional and other forms of slavery still exist today in society and in your own mind. Free yourself one Self Care Baby Step at a time. If you are facing a critical breakdown in a particular category of care, the comfort you feel for the normal will never compare to the peaceful sweet taste of being free from living in a state of crisis. Keep going and stay free. Remain a Self Care Revolutionary forever.

Why a Self Care Revolution Story Matters

With the physical and emotional scar tissue remaining from my surgery, I use my self-care strategies so that I am able to continue moving forward with seeing myself as beautiful and stay healthy more often. I do not give up, run and hide anymore. I am now able to retrace my same steps to freedom when I need them. I feel less lost in the wilderness of emotions and I don't faking it throughout the day anymore without addressing a critical self-care need. Those triggered moments that bring me back to that operating table, the recovery and trying to pretend to be okay around others while truly being sad have lessened tremendously. I feel no requirement to pretend for prolonged periods of time now because I know, when I am alone there is something I can do to begin feeling better all on my own. I don't stay stuck in a loop forever analyzing my own problems, fussing about them and discussing them over and over again. I break my A.F.D. Loops with each Self Care Baby Step I take.

I am not holding out for a friend, parent or partner to save me anymore when my needs are critical. One challenging event after another in the past would typically trigger in me thoughts of hopelessness that used to spiral out of control and emotionally paralyze me. I would disconnect and hide from addressing my critical needs and more importantly I would not ask for help.

My personal self-care revolution story matters because I began to understand my mother more after this experience. I began to have more compassion for her and all women still fighting to find a quilt hanging in a window for them. I have compassion for all women fighting to free themselves their own emotional slavery.

My mother has given birth five times. My maternal grandmother gave birth eleven times. I could go on tracing my lineage and sharing stories of women who have endured even more than I. Their self-care revolution story matters. What it feels like to not really have recovered physically or emotionally from one blow before absorbing another is a feeling we women know all too well. This life of surviving from one struggle to the next is not living for a man or woman.

Chronic depression, daily struggle and trauma in our community, the black community, is deemed acceptable in our world today. Although we use music culture and the celebration of our strength to move on, suffering and trauma is accepted as the norm for us.

It has been deemed acceptable for us live in lack while still loving and caring for each other. It is deemed acceptable that life be hard for black people. We have seen depression and broken spirits through mental illness over and over again in our community so much so it is deemed normal. When depression is deemed normal, the desire to live better, healthier and more healed is not welcomed. When depression, shame and just getting by is the norm, companies develop products to support that norm. I don't want that life and no matter your gender or race, I don't want that life for you.

I developed a compassion for my mother I never had before after delivering my son. I developed a softness towards her I never had before. I carried two children in my belly, lost one and suffered while delivering the other. My mother has gone through unspeakable challenges her life. Some of her challenges I will never know and nor what tenderness was missing for her in those moments. What support was missing for her? My parents, grandparents and great grandparents faced traumas I will never know and they still loved us, fed us, fought for us and survived. My father raised me with no role model for himself. What compassion and support existed from him? Who saw a black male single father's face and saw someone deserving of compassion?

My experience with trauma opened up a whole world to me I never knew and an understanding of my people I never fully understood until then. We are traumatized as people physically and psychologically everyday yet, we are not allowed to respond as such. Through the blessing of the arts we are able to be free however in our day to day lives we struggle.

We are employed by those who typically have no patience nor compassion for our struggles. We employ each other with the expectation of behaving 'normal' and covering up our pains and struggles long enough to get the job done. This is the day in and day out grind and process compacting the pain of unhealed spirits in one place with no reprieve in sight. Our only true freedom throughout an entire day lies in each revolutionary self-care move we make one day, hour and moment at a time. This is freedom. Each self-care choice is our freedom.

I would read about slavery as a child and as a college student. I read about the seasoning of slaves in Louisiana and the stories of torture endured by men, women and children yet, I had not experienced a trauma like the one I experienced during my delivery at that time. I knew through factual historic accounts, we have not only been traumatized repeatedly and continue to be traumatized but that we are also forced to live in an environment where the daily traumas, pains and micro-aggressions we endure are spoken about with no compassion. How do you find your own Underground Railroad to freedom, when everything around you say emotional slavery should be normal? How do you find a safe place to heal when your work and home life may be benefiting from your silence?

As a people are fighting to heal every day in a country that does acknowledge nor repair the centuries of profit made off of our pain. From slavery to prison systems, our healing and growth has never been a goal for those profiting off of our pain. How do you even find the desire to take care of yourself when it is shown to you through documentaries like Ava Duveray's 13th that it is acceptable and profitable to continue breaking a heartbroken people?

This self-care revolution is possible. I wanted to offer an alternative to faking it through the day. I wanted begin by offering my self-care revolution story and campaign as a prayerful inspiration to create and share your own self-care revolution. Break the entrapment of emotional slavery. Find your path to freedom from embarrassment and shame by asking for help when you need it.

Even though I communicated I could still feel on that operating room table and could not get anyone to help or believe me, I still survived. I will do more than survive. That experience did not break me. That experience taught me to speak louder when I need something. I will flip over tables and completely cause a scene now if it means I will have a critical need like not enduring complete surgery with no working anesthesia. I will take care of myself.

Although though my low self-care choices have planted seeds of behaviors I am still plucking out one painful moment at a time, I will do more than just survive. I will take care of myself. Even though I have seen a history of family members suffering in silence, I will do more than just survive. Even though the television and internet is riddled with messages that I am not worth much, I will do more than survive.

I will take care of myself. I was terrified to create a program, write a book for the first time and launch a Self Care Day movement, and I did it anyway. I will do more than just survive. I will take care of myself because my ancestors paid the price for me work harder to free myself from the invisible and residual effect of slavery that continue to this day. Emotional slavery exists. Embarrassment and shame as a form of emotional slavery exists. It is popular. It is used frequently. It is accepted. It is destroyable. I am now gentle with myself. I forgive myself and with each self-care step, I am establishing self-worth. The feeling of helplessness, fear and pain I felt on that table taught me I am a survivor. What I did after that experience taught me I am a Self Care Revolutionary and so are you. /#selfcarerevolutionary/

Self Care Stories

This appendix contains personal, unedited stories by people who have applied the Self Care Plan to their lives.

What I Know to Be True -- A Self Care Story by Candice McKinley, Esq.

It was sudden and scary. I found myself on the bathroom floor face down not knowing that I had just fainted. I woke up to my mother screaming to call 911 and my Atlanta Tri Divas teammates surrounding me with concern written on their faces. I finally came to and adamantly told them that I did not want to go the emergency room. My mind told me that I had overexerted myself in the pool doing drills as I prepared for the triathlon--not knowing at the time what was really going on with me.

I cautiously gathered myself with the help of my loving mother who drove me home to rest. My head pounding, my lip bleeding, and my knee bruised I kept telling myself that was going to be ok. I never was one to go to an emergency room or really have any serious illness at all. Not feeling completely well, I headed to work the next morning fighting through the pain in my head. In my mind, I thought that I could not show signs of illness because my first solo trial was the next day. My client and my senior partners were counting on me to take care of the case. I was putting the needs of others before my own while rationalizing to myself that is what I was supposed to do at the time. Then God intervened at work and took the trial off the calendar. My client had a death in the family--I no longer had the responsibility on my plate. Yet, I still thought I could make it back to work again to finish some files the following day.

My Aunt Maretis assisted that she drive me to work because she never saw me look so "out of it" before. At work, my head pain became unbearable. My friend, co-worker, and self-care expert, Ms. Anana Parris, took one look at me and demanded that I leave the job and go straight to the hospital. She is one of my angel's on Earth. She actually saved me from a complete medical crisis. Another angel, my Aunt Maretis picked me up and drove me straight to the hospital. I was diagnosed as a critically anemic patient and needed an immediate blood transfusion. I was released a couple of days later and found myself back in the hospital a few days later in need of another blood transfusion.

In less than a week, I thought my whole life had changed for the worst. No longer could I think about everything and everyone around me and what they needed. I was forced to think of my health and how to get better. My mindset had to change from this experience being the worst to it being a serious wake up call. To understand my health condition, listen to my body, and not be so stubborn to getting help. The lesson I learned is that when your body speaks to you— really listen to it—it is trying to tell you something important.

As I recover with the help of my family, I see clearly now that paying attention to health signs before it becomes critical is vital. Regardless of what I have to do in my daily routine as a mother, a young lawyer, and always on the go person—I must not lose sight of myself. If I am not healthy enough for myself, I cannot do all that I need to do for my family and clients.

I am so appreciative of the angels/self-care warrior women I have around me like my Mother, Aunt, and Anana who saw what I need before I could for myself. Simply to get assistance, slow down, and take care of myself. God's plan for me is already written and this experience is part of my life's journey. I will heal myself by understanding my condition and how to live with it. Also, think positive affirmations of healthiness, continuously seek out materials and individuals who will enhance my life of wholeness.

"In the infinity of life where I am, all is perfect, whole, and complete. Each one of us myself included, experiences the richness of life in ways that are meaningful to us. I now look at the past with love and choose to learn from my old experiences. There is no right or wrong, nor good or bad. The past is over and done. There is only the experiences of the moment. I love myself for bringing myself through this past into this present moment. I share what and who I am, for I know we are all one in Spirit. All is well in my world." Louise L. Hay

Paying Up -- A Self Care Story by Sunnye Braitwaite

I faced a fear this week, surprised as I confronted this fear that ate at my financial stability for decades. I did something I had never done in my real adulthood---I made a promise to a bill collector. Now, at 34 I could only, if I focused, tell you why I have never had a conversation with a bill collector longer than 3 seconds. I've never knowingly picked up a call from a bill collector; until yesterday. I answered this call from the hospital trying to convince myself it could be about something else while betting it was about a bill. My bet was right. The rep asked me if I was able to pay, did I know what amount, etc. What happened next surprised me---I took financial responsibility. I let the rep know I would check with my insurance company about what was covered or not and then call the hospital back to set up a payment plan. And I meant it.

This month I designated my focus to financial matters: budgeting, financial literacy, and savings. As I gave attention to formal goals, I also checked off things I didn't include, surprised that the theme of the month took on a life of its own, sweeping up goals I had never taken time or been successful in achieving, largely to fear masking as procrastination or avoidance. Owning my self-care journey has made owning my full presence much, much easier. That's all, folks.

A Work In Progress -- Self Care Story by Adrienne Rowe

Hello Anana:

I just wanted to share my story. So I believe we met in October when I began having migraines more regularly. I told you and the other women who came to the AfriSalsa [Self Care Support Group] session. You then lovingly gave me your self-care soap that read, "I welcome healing in my life." I kept it on my bathroom sink and used it religiously. Until now that lemon grass sent makes me think of healing.

Unfortunately after the day that I shared my story I didn't get better, but instead got worse. I ended up having to take a two and a half month medical leave from my job. The migraines became so debilitating that

I literally could barely walk or talk. I went to several doctors before getting relief.

The thing that stood out to me from the saying on my soap, was that I should focus more of my energy on my healing than I should my illness. As my medical leave continued I slowly began focusing my time on loving me. I focused my time on caring for me. I decided not to worry about my future AS MUCH. (I'm a work in progress).

It has now been close to two months since I've had a migraine and I thank God! I'm not sure if it was intentional that the self-care soap that you gave me today read, "I am beautiful AND MY BODY IS HEALTHY!" When I read it again at home it almost brought tears of joy to my eyes as it is SO applicable to my life today!

Thank you. I pray that God continues to bless your ministry!

Mirror Mirror -- A Self Care Story by Mr. Bub Adewumi, Business Owner <u>Amarachi Lounge, Brooklyn NY</u>

I looked at myself in the mirror one day and got on the scale, I thought about my three children and said it's time to make a change. I owed my family a long life so I had to train myself on how to love foods and drinks that are low in sugar, and high on the Good stuff. Finding the time to go to the gym is pointless with my work schedule so loving to eat and drink things that are good for me have to bring me happiness! So every time I order salmon with garlic spinach over the steak and mashed potatoes, I shake my head and smile to the goodness!

No Simple Wash -- A Self Care Story by Charity Jordan

I sat on a friends couch distraught but too distracted to cry. Somehow my greatest accomplishment, giving birth to two amazing children, had made me loose myself. Now I know that "loosing yourself" is a common cliché used by new moms but for me it was real. I was depressed due to dehydration and physically sick due to exhaustion, however my self-care revelation came at the realization that I was no longer doing a basic step in my hygiene regimen... I wasn't washing my face.

Perhaps this sounds small to some, but for me, washing my face had been a special ritual that I had completed daily since puberty. I put extra special effort into picking out the perfect products with the best reviews. I made sure to layer them just right daily, cleanser/toner/moisturizer, and weekly treated myself to a mask. Now I had LOST myself in breastmilk and Barney and did not even own a face bar. I was just not taking care of my face but my whole self. Devotions, nutrition, and relationships had all been cast away in the dirty diapers.

But Ms. Parris took my hand and walked me through a Self Care plan to re-find myself. What were my basic needs? We started with just drinking water, added in a few hours of childcare so that I could eat, pray, and sleep, then finally reached washing my face. You see it was not only my face that was being cleansed during those few moments of soapy time in the mirror but also my soul. Looking at my reflection daily I remembered my value, my victories, and my voice."

Charity Jordan @1uncensoredMom, *Creator & Executive Producer*

Anana's Self Care Revolution Story

We all have our own personal Underground Railroad journey to emotional freedom story in life that called for a self-care revolution. A story that speaks to our raw desire for freedom when everything around us didn't support us taking care of ourselves but we did it anyway. A story of and within our lives that is still being written as we continue to face one difficult experience after another. One day at a time we work to escape from the emotional slavery in our own lives.

We all have a story of a challenging or traumatic experience that resurfaces sometimes when triggered bringing us back to that moment as if it happened yesterday. When the story resurfaces, we feel afraid as if the danger is still there, when it's not. We remember the physical pain as if it just happened. Then, we emotionally respond to people as if they had something to do with it when they didn't. Yep, we all have a story. A story of emotional slavery that we try to escape over and over again. We try to escape the feelings and emotions attached to those experiences, only to be dragged back kicking and screaming. We try to avoid or ignore the terrifying emotions felt while being enslaved in what's horrible about the story by distracting ourselves just to cope. While all the while, the sad and scary emotions of the story are lingering there. They are watching us live our lives, ready to resurface like a pacing, whip carrying, and overseeing slave master riding a horse on a hot day. As soon as we get a taste of a way to free ourselves from the pain of the trauma, the whip cracks and without a scuffle we are reminded our place. The unhealed emotional trauma wins and we are back to the day to day plantation life of hiding our trauma.

Someone asks, "Hey how are you today?" and you hear the whip crack so you reply in a forced peppy voice, "I'm fine how are you?" It still hurts though. You remember your story of trauma even though you fight to hide it on your walk into work. It still hurts. To battle this, our stories only communicating the pain must turn into stories of freedom with moments of extreme revolutionary self-care interlaced through it. Moments of self-care become our safe places along our own Underground Railroad to emotional freedom in life.

We look for the quilts to be hung in windows of those who recognize the critical need for self-care and support in our lives. Those who know that self-care is form of social justice are especially equipped to house you when you need a moment. We look for direction from those who can guide us to our next safe place on our self-care journey to emotional freedom. To have freedom you must have the desire for freedom. Many have the desire for Araminta (commonly known as Harriet Tubman) to save them from their pain more than they have the desire to be their own Araminta. To have emotional freedom you have to want to free yourself while searching out and hunting for those secret coded quilts hanging in the windows signifying a safe place for us to rest, eat, heal and get a new direction again on our journey to emotional freedom. A safe place without judgement or shame is waiting for you even if you can't see it.

Sometimes it takes a traumatic experience to expose just how emotionally enslaved we are. There are moments in our life that hit us so hard, we don't know what to do. We don't know to look for safe places and people to help us to heal. This is my self-care revolution story.

I showed up for my standard ultrasound appointment amazingly on time. After a leisurely wait in the pregnancy magazine filled lobby of my doctor's office, I headed back for the greasy, slimy, ice cold rub around ultrasound session to see my baby. Calmly sitting next to his high-rise sun shining window, my doctor said I was leaking fluid and needed to be induced that very day. He said my baby was fine. I remember hearing about how they starve pregnant women in hospitals during delivery to protect them from issues during surgery so, I promptly made a food stop on my way to then Crawford Long Hospital on Peachtree Street. My hand wrapped around the door handle with excitement at Papi's on Ponce de Leon St. in Atlanta. I placed my usual delicious order for a Cuban fish sandwich and sweet plantains before waddling in to the hospital. I was not concerned or worried. I even passed my friend and phenomenal musician Dash and his mother along the way. I was enormous and often was asked if I was carrying twins. My big boy had free room, board and meals but it was now time for him to be evicted and I was ready!

I checked in as a big ole 10 months pregnant woman with my first child and my greatest fear wasn't contractions but an epidural needle. I saw the movie "The Business of Being Born", had birthing classes, was mature to the ripe age of 35, ate very well and danced regularly to stay in shape but none of that could have prepared me for what was about to happen.

The hospital did what American hospitals usually do by aggressively inducing my labor unnaturally. With this being my first delivery, I truly was too afraid to take a stand when it was time. So, after my son's heartbeat stopped a second time, the decision was made to do a C-section because he wasn't budging much. I didn't even imagine I would ever need a C-section. I heard about them but didn't think I'd need to prepare for one. It never ever crossed my mind as a possibility for me.

After 24hrs of natural labor pains and contractions enhanced by Pitocin, I could barely breathe without the oxygen mask. I waited, terrified of that epidural needle. Some of my friends like Ayana Perkins, Adinah and her awesome sister with the foot massage, Kim, my husband and my mother-in-law Isabel were by my side. I found a happy place on the moon when I saw the needle in a sterile bag enter the room.

Once returning back to earth, I laid back... and felt a contraction. I was never afraid to speak up for myself so I let everyone know,

"I can still feel the contractions." The anesthesiologist returned three additional times to administer three additional doses and yet I could still feel. I tried to convince them over and over again I could still feel. The decision was made to increase the dosage of Pitocin and not soon after my son's heart stopped a third time and was not coming back.

"Code Pink!" one nurse yelled as they all raced in seemingly from nowhere. I looked back towards my friends as the nurses raised the rails and adjusted my bed for emergency transport and saw terrified tears from my family and friends. I looked to my left and said to my husband, who was soon swept away to be prepped for the OR, *"I can still feel."*

The nurses wheeled me into the operating room and I said to the anesthesiologist, again, *"I can still feel"*.

He said *"are you sure it's not just pressure?"*

I said, *"No, I can feel the contractions and the baby."*

The doctors and nurses rushed to beat the clock as his heart had not been beating since I left my hospital room. I looked around with my oxygen mask on and got scared. What else can I do.? What else can I say?

I looked up in fear at the only face I saw and heard the anesthesiologist say, "*See, you can't feel because they just started cutting. If you could feel you would be coming off this table right now.*"

I said to him muffled through the mask, "*I can't feel my skin but I can feel on the inside.*"

No one listened. They parted my tummy, reached in to the open wound of my body to grab my son. I felt the worst pain of my life. Hands were inside my body, moving around organs, pulling at my son and hurting me. I remember how sensitive and painful everything felt. My insides felt tender to the touch and they touched everything. It seemed to last forever. I didn't know how to stop it from hurting. Immediately, I wrestled and broke the straps of the operating table harness trying to get up, run or hold myself together somehow. I don't remember screaming. I don't remember talking. I only remember the pain.

People started yelling and holding me down while saying in distorted unison, "give her the ... give it to her now!" I don't know what 'it' was but I thought I was dying because soon, with the pain and hands holding my arms, shoulders and head, the sound started going in and out. My vision became blurry and inconsistent. At the time, we chose to wait to find out what the sex of the baby was. I fought the pain and the drifting effects of the drug long enough to catch a slight glimpse of my baby. I just wanted to know if I was having a boy or a girl. Through the pain, the fear and grabbing of my baby, I found out had a son then blacked out.

I awakened briefly in the middle of the surgery. I heard talks of which nurse was going to the movies and when. Weekend plans while sewing me up were discussed but I felt nothing. I didn't feel my baby. I didn't feel pain. I felt nothing. I awakened a second time in a small recovery room. EKG monitors beeps and an ugly plain blue thin blanket was over me. A nurse came in and asked how I was doing. I said, "How is my baby? Do I have a boy?" She said yes. She said the cord was wrapped twice around his neck and he survived anyway.

I asked her to bring him to me and she said I couldn't until I could move my legs. I couldn't. I had so many doses of the epidural, it took me an hour to wiggle a toe. I cried intermittently until one of my dear friends and Self Care Dream Team members Kim Brundidge came in. She said she was proud of me. She said my baby was doing push-ups in the nursery. She said I did well. Other friends came by to stay with me until I could move my legs. Then they brought me my baby boy. He was perfect. We survived and this is how my self-care revolution story begins.

This was many years ago and yet, I remember everything vividly. At the time, my physical recovery from the C-section was difficult and longer than expected to say the least but my emotional and spiritual recovery felt like it would never happen. I was lost because what previously worked didn't and no one believed me. I did what I was supposed to do and it didn't work. I spoke up and no one believed me. It was painful, terrifying and preventable. No one listened and no one believed me. One trauma piled on top of other challenges and I was wheeled out the door of the hospital lost with a newborn baby. This one act of delivering a baby, done many centuries by billions of women across the globe had broken me. This one moment of my life shattered what I believed I could survive... and yet, I survived anyway. We survived anyway. We left the hospital two days later.

I had post-partum depression, self-diagnosed post-traumatic stress disorder... post everything and a new baby.

My mama, grandmothers nor great-grandmothers could be there. I was nursing by myself alone while my husband was at work 7:00am − 7:00pm generally six days a week. The baby, my cellphone, some food, my stitches and I all stayed alone together in the bed throughout the entire day. Just us. Then, it happened. My awakening to what I needed was about to happen. My realization that I was enslaved by the thought being embarrassed I needed help became apparent to me in one critical moment.

My baby, my stitches and I were shuffling along slowly one day, trying to make it to the bathroom. My foot got caught on a raised section of our one bedroom laminate floor condo and it pulled on the fresh stitches across my lower abdomen as if a pair hands had come up from the floor personally to yank them. The Percocet was not fully working because I had an infection I didn't realize I had. For nearly two weeks I had gotten used to pain. This particular pain paired with the pull from the floor to my stitches was so great that right in front of the bathroom door, my two week old son slipped straight out of my hands and began dropping. I forgot my pain throwing my body forward. My hands slid under his bottom and head in just enough time to graze the floor with my knuckles and break his fall. I stood frozen in time, heart beating loud and bent over in pain. I was in shock holding him still. He did not cry. He did not whimper. He smiled.

I didn't have the strength to stand up right away, so I stayed, bent over cradling his warm brown body crying. I almost dropped my baby. In complete terror, I immediately enacted my first critical self-care act that would begin my journey of revolutionary self-care. I realized I needed help.

Squinting my face and eyes from the pain, I slowly lifted him and myself up. We shuffled to the bed and I grabbed my cell phone. I thought of 10 friends and sent out a 911 text. I literally typed to a crew of girlfriends

"911 help. In pain I almost dropped the baby. Please help."

Like a flurry of brown multi-hued angels, five of my dearest friends arrived at my doorstep in 20 minutes. They changed the sheets on my bed, held the baby while I napped, mopped the floors, made me tea and listened to my birth story. They did things I didn't know I needed done. They were my self-care angels that day. When I could not care for myself, they cared for me. At my lowest point they held me and my son. I not only learned I was loved, I learned I had the ability to ask for help. I learned I had the ability through asking for help to take care of myself while caring for my son.

My intellectual, punitive and unforgiving side took over when they left. Why didn't I arrange for a doula to be there after my birth? I could have been much more aggressive about my self-care long before almost dropping my first born. What stopped me? What was wrong with me? What thoughts were going through my head that made me think I was not worthy of support and care. Why didn't I make the connection early on that if I'm not ok my son won't be ok?

The questions were unrelenting. As the days passed I had to sit with myself and think. I knew something was missing and I didn't know what that was. How had I gone 35 years and not known what I critically needed in one of the most important moments of my life? After seeing the help I really needed show up, I continued beating myself up for some time. I had to begin realizing that sheer ignorance, a society promoting a lack of gentleness towards women and a lifestyle of being too embarrassed to ask for help played a big part.

I had no clue I was so enslaved by the thought of feeling embarrassed about asking for help. What was taught to me was women delivered babies all the time. Women pushed forward until they collapsed, especially black women and men all the time. It became very clear very quickly to me that suffering alone and in silence had been what I knew to be the norm for myself and my people.

After almost dropping my new born, I began to spiral. I felt I had no options. The depression started setting in the more the isolation from others continued. All this love, support and care showed up at my door but it was gone again just as fast as it arrived. I was alone with a baby, again. My thoughts became hopeless because I now knew what I needed and I didn't know how I could create it for myself on a consistent basis. The physical pain wasn't subsiding and the duration of pain was too much to bear. My understanding and acceptance of suffering alone had caused me to allow a full infection to grow to several organs next to my uterus without me knowing it.

I laid there in the home, painfully breastfeeding for the first time as I brainstormed what to do. Nothing I learned growing up prepared me for this. I knew how to cheer myself up in college with a strawberry cheesecake after finals. I knew how to go salsa dancing after the end of a relationship and I knew how to get to a West African dance rehearsal after a long day of work in corporate America. I learned so fast why a grandmother or family member is sorely needed after a birth and I was sad about not having it.

Church was a place I went to not a lifestyle I brought home with me at that time. Church also did not offer options that were supporting my critical immediate needs. I don't recall the painful nursing chapter in the bible. There was no "post-partum you can't walk right after a C-section" ministry at the church I attended.

Most of my friends worked during the days or had their own kids and challenges to address. I had no idea how to take care of myself in this way with this responsibility. I was never ever prepared for this. Ten months of discomfort, a delivery experience that seemed like a Lifetime movie special and a new life that needed to feed from me all day all by myself.

My thoughts began to spiral into 'what's the point'. I was too afraid to call anyone cause I assumed their answer would be 'no' and I would be embarrassed /#selfcareblock/. Minute by minute the loneliness and duration of pain tipped the scales to scary thoughts of me not wanting to be here anymore. Without asking for help or calling my doctor, I had blocked myself from getting what I needed. Blocking a critical need in any category of your life eventually leads to self-care suicide in that category.

I shuffled to the mirror and looked at myself with tears in my eyes. This was a moment I could go right or left. Live or die. Prolonged pain, loneliness and depression was winning. I had no manual. I had no instructions. I had no guidance. While looking in the bathroom mirror, looked at myself and asked God for help. I heard nothing. I asked again then said out loud, *"What did you used to do Anana? What helped before? What did you do? You can figure this out. It's getting too bad."*

I talked it out like a moving prayer and said, *"My thoughts need to change. What do I need? I need the pain to stop. I need to not think hopeless thoughts."*

I wanted freedom. Freedom from the physical pain and freedom from the emotional pain. It is important that you want freedom from emotional slavery. Slavery isn't designed for you to get better. Learning to live with pain doesn't get better, you merely eventually die from it. I wanted freedom from feeling lost, afraid and embarrassed about not knowing what to do. I spoke out loud what I needed.

My tiny baby boy was asleep. I stared into my own eyes and remembered I used to hang affirmations in my mirror./#emotionalselfcare/ The words I hung in the mirror, needed to be something that would address what I felt the worst about. So I said out loud in the mirror, "*I am beautiful and my body is healthy*". Buckets of tears came from seemingly nowhere and did not stop. I knew those were the words. I also knew if I hung that piece of paper on my mirror, it would look tacky and between the baby baths and hand washing it would melt those words right off the paper. I thought to myself, "*Ok Anana, you need those words to be in something practical that you do every day.*" An idea hit me after a dream. I wished the words could be in clear soap and every time I wash my hands I could say them out loud. Who knew how to make that happen? I had never seen that so I needed to call one of my genius artist friends to tell her my idea and find out how in the world this could happen. This artistic self-care homework assignment was giving me something progressive that addressed a critical need to focus my mind on other than giving up. I had a self-care baby step. I had a piece of a self-care plan.

The mission of creating a self-care based soap became my lifeline because I needed it. I needed the creative expression. I needed to know those words would be closer to me and used in a greater way one day. This mission of an affirmation in a product I needed anyway became my first self-care project. It was the first component of developing a formal Self Care Plan for myself and others that would take nearly three years to craft.

My first step and safe place stop on my own Underground Railroad was calling the dynamically talented artist Kottavei, now artistic Self Care Dream Team member. She made me feel safe to explore a creative idea that could help me. She offered me what seemed to be a secret code to getting where I wanted to be. I wanted to be artistically capable of creating my soap. Kottavei metaphorically sewed directions in a quilt for me to know where to go next on my journey to getting what I needed. She helped me get the nourishment I needed to make it until my next stop on my own Underground Railroad self-care journey. I explained to her the details of the soap and she helped me craft the answer. In the next three painful weeks I named my son, visited the doctor to heal my infection and created my first self-care soap called *niara* (meaning one of high purpose). I wanted this soap to be more than soap for me. It had a high purpose with its words to help heal and free me from emotional slavery.

I started using my soap saying my affirmation out loud and looking in the mirror while washing my hands,

"I am beautiful and my body is healthy."

"I am beautiful and my body is healthy."

"I am beautiful and my body is healthy."

"I am beautiful and my body is healthy."

For the first week I think I cried every single time. I couldn't believe I really *didn't* believe what I was saying. After the second week it got a little better. By the third week I was believing it. I realized this self-care soap, was a self-care tool that I had weaved into my lifestyle to address my critical needs. By layering a daily ritual like washing my hands with a self-care act like saying words I really needed to believe, I was helping to heal and free myself faster. /#selfcareisfreedom/ I really needed to be free from feeling bad about myself. It became a new habit. My thoughts began to change. My lifestyle began to change. I realized the path for my own personal Underground Railroad to escape my emotional slavery of depression, embarrassment and sadness was a focused and strategic Self Care Plan. I needed to be honest about my needs, ask for help along the way and find as many safe places to work on my self-care needs as possible. My body healed. My stitches dissolved. My son is growing and I am using the same path to freedom over and over again. This was my personal self-care revolution story.

Why A Self Care Revolution Story Matters

With the physical and emotional scar tissue remaining from my surgery, I use my self-care strategies so that I am able to continue moving forward with seeing myself as beautiful and stay healthy more often. I do not give up, run and hide anymore. I am now able to retrace my same steps to freedom when I need them. I feel less lost in the wilderness of emotions and I don't faking it throughout the day anymore without addressing a critical self-care need. Those triggered moments that bring me back to that operating table, the recovery and trying to pretend to be okay around others while truly being sad have lessened tremendously. I feel no requirement to pretend for prolonged periods of time now because I know, when I am alone there is something I can do to begin feeling better all on my own. I don't stay stuck in a loop forever analyzing my own problems, fussing about them and discussing them over and over again. I break my A.F.D. Loops with each Self Care Baby Step I take.

I am not holding out for a friend, parent or partner to save me anymore when my needs are critical. One challenging event after another in the past would typically trigger in me thoughts of hopelessness that used to spiral out of control and emotionally paralyze me. I would disconnect and hide from addressing my critical needs and more importantly I would not ask for help.

My personal self-care revolution story matters because I began to understand my mother more after this experience. I began to have more compassion for her and all women still fighting to find a quilt hanging in a window for them. I have compassion for all women fighting to free themselves their own emotional slavery.

My mother has given birth five times. My maternal grandmother gave birth eleven times. I could go on tracing my lineage and sharing stories of women who have endured even more than I. Their self-care revolution story matters. What it feels like to not really have recovered physically or emotionally from one blow before absorbing another is a feeling we women know all too well. This life of surviving from one struggle to the next is not living for a man or woman.

Chronic depression, daily struggle and trauma in our community, the black community, is deemed acceptable in our world today. Although we use music culture and the celebration of our strength to move on, suffering and trauma is accepted as the norm for us.

It has been deemed acceptable for us live in lack while still loving and caring for each other. It is deemed acceptable that life be hard for black people. We have seen depression and broken spirits through mental illness over and over again in our community so much so it is deemed normal. When depression is deemed normal, the desire to live better, healthier and more healed is not welcomed. When depression, shame and just getting by is the norm, companies develop products to support that norm. I don't want that life and no matter your gender or race, I don't want that life for you.

I developed a compassion for my mother I never had before after delivering my son. I developed a softness towards her I never had before. I carried two children in my belly, lost one and suffered while delivering the other. My mother has gone through unspeakable challenges her life. Some of her challenges I will never know and nor what tenderness was missing for her in those moments. What support was missing for her? My parents, grandparents and great grandparents faced traumas I will never know and they still loved us, fed us, fought for us and survived. My father raised me with no role model for himself. What compassion and support existed from him? Who saw a black male single father's face and saw someone deserving of compassion?

My experience with trauma opened up a whole world to me I never knew and an understanding of my people I never fully understood until then. We are traumatized as people physically and psychologically everyday yet, we are not allowed to respond as such. Through the blessing of the arts we are able to be free however in our day to day lives we struggle.

We are employed by those who typically have no patience nor compassion for our struggles. We employ each other with the expectation of behaving 'normal' and covering up our pains and struggles long enough to get the job done. This is the day in and day out grind and process compacting the pain of unhealed spirits in one place with no reprieve in sight. Our only true freedom throughout an entire day lies in each revolutionary self-care move we make one day, hour and moment at a time. This is freedom. Each self-care choice is our freedom.

I would read about slavery as a child and as a college student. I read about the seasoning of slaves in Louisiana and the stories of torture endured by men, women and children yet, I had not experienced a trauma like the one I experienced during my delivery at that time. I knew through factual historic accounts, we have not only been traumatized repeatedly and continue to be traumatized but that we are also forced to live in an environment where the daily traumas, pains and micro-aggressions we endure are spoken about with no compassion. How do you find your own Underground Railroad to freedom, when everything around you say emotional slavery should be normal? How do you find a safe place to heal when your work and home life may be benefiting from your silence?

As a people are fighting to heal every day in a country that does acknowledge nor repair the centuries of profit made off of our pain. From slavery to prison systems, our healing and growth has never been a goal for those profiting off of our pain. How do you even find the desire to take care of yourself when it is shown to you through documentaries like Ava Duveray's 13th that it is acceptable and profitable to continue breaking a heartbroken people.

This self-care revolution is possible. I wanted to offer an alternative to faking it through the day. I wanted begin by offering my self-care revolution story and campaign as a prayerful inspiration to create and share your own self-care revolution. Break the entrapment of emotional slavery. Find your path to freedom from embarrassment and shame by asking for help when you need it.

Even though I communicated I could still feel on that operating room table and could not get anyone to help or believe me, I still survived. I will do more than survive. That experience did not break me. That experience taught me to speak louder when I need something. I will flip over tables and completely cause a scene now if it means I will have a critical need like not enduring complete surgery with no working anesthesia. I will take care of myself.

Although though my low self-care choices have planted seeds of behaviors I am still plucking out one painful moment at a time, I will do more than just survive. I will take care of myself. Even though I have seen a history of family members suffering in silence, I will do more than just survive. Even though the television and internet is riddled with messages that I am not worth much, I will do more than survive.

I will take care of myself. I was terrified to create a program, write a book for the first time and launch a Self Care Day movement, and I did it anyway. I will do more than just survive. I will take care of myself because my ancestors paid the price for me work harder to free myself from the invisible and residual effect of slavery that continue to this day. Emotional slavery exists. Embarrassment and shame as a form of emotional slavery exists. It is popular. It is used frequently. It is accepted. It is destroyable. I am now gentle with myself. I forgive myself and with each self-care step, I am establishing self-worth. The feeling of helplessness, fear and pain I felt on that table taught me I am a survivor. What I did after that experience taught me I am a Self Care Revolutionary and so are you. /#selfcarerevolutionary/

Self Care Revolutionary Activity: My Self Care Story

Use this form to begin to write your own Self Care story.

Growing up, I saw _____ as a major image of excellent (pick a care category) _____ self-care. Today, I believe I like to _____ as a result of my upbringing. When I was younger, I believed self-care meant _____. Now I understand that self-care means _____ for me.

A major shift in my ability to spiritually and emotionally take care of myself happened when _____.

Now, my greatest (pick a care category) _____ self-care challenges are _____. The people, environments and scenarios that most challenge my spiritual and emotional self-care are _____. When I take a moment to reflect on my spiritual and emotional health, I think

_____.

My (pick a care category) _____

Dream Team Member(s) include _____.

So far, after working on my (pick a care category)

_____ self-care, I have learned

_____. Activities the help support

my (pick a care category) _____ self-

care include _____. If I

ever experience a traumatic experience, I would like

to remember _____. Moving

forward, I will remember that my top (pick a care

category) _____ self-care activities

that need to remain in my life are

_____.

I am grateful for these people and experiences

_____

_____.

30 Days of Self Care Thoughts

Read one thought a day to encourage you on your self-care journey. If this is your only self-care act in a day, you have done well. Put new thoughts in your head every day to fight the overt and subliminal messages set to keep you from moving forward. Keep going. Self-care is revolutionary.

Day 1

Even when you are sad it's important to surround yourself with joy so it can infiltrate you without a big effort from you. Get out and be around joy. That is social self-care.

Day 2

What if you woke up today, set one Self Care Goal, small or large, and achieved it TODAY.

Day 3

Checking a critical self-care item off the list will feel better than running away from it... trust me.

Day 4

Be aware of how people make you feel. Stay around those who support your Self Care Plan when you are working a critical phase of the plan. It is how you achieve your goal in one piece.

Day 5

Social Activism is Self Care. Today bills are being heard that affect our safety and ability to have accountability, transparency and compassion from the police and government representatives. Become active today as a form of self-care. Join an organization and add to the momentum.

Day 6

You have the power to take a Self Care Baby Step in your most challenging Self Care Category. Take 1 today.

Day 7

Keep getting stronger every day. Do a little more every day. Just a little more.... then a lot more.... then a little more ... then a little more ... then a lot more.

Day 8

Good lovin' is also lying in bed running through all the acts of self-care you can do to yourself today. Every touch to your soul and body feels better when you have primed it for enjoyment with excellent self-care. Now go check good lovin off your list today with each and every self-care act you can squeeze in a day. Make it good ones you will never forget.

Day 9

Let out a cry, then keep going!

Day 10

Self-care is based on a need. What do you need today?

Day 11

Once you get a taste of working your own Self Care Plan... anything or anyone in your life that benefits when you don't take care of yourself will soon be missing out, and that is ok.

Day 12

Each Self Care Baby Step helps your self-care journey get easier and easier and helps your self-care muscle get stronger and stronger. Take ONE today.

Day 13

With love let them know your need (not want) is critical at this time and for your soul, spirit, finances, body or mind to be healthy you must take better care of yourself.

Day 14

Sometimes we need help changing our thoughts. Take your Self Care Baby Step today by saying. I nourish myself, do my best, say thank you and release the rest.

Day 15

You can do it!! Post, share or talk to someone kind, gentle and trustworthy about your self-care today.

Day 16

A Self Care Plan is how you fight for yourself when it feels like no one is fighting for you.

Day 17

Participate in your own self-care until embarrassment nor fear stops you from reaching your goal. Ask for help and welcome guidance.

Day 18

One great thing about a Self Care Plans is when you get started as a parent, child, friend or spouse you realize you are not just addressing your own care but modeling it for those you care about. You are teaching them all what you need and that you are worthy.

Day 19

Self Care Planning is about caring for yourself while caring for others. It should always be synonymous.

Day 20

Sometimes life just sucker punches us and it takes a moment to catch our breath. While gathering ourselves we can check out physically, emotionally economically and other ways. Self Care Planning helps you check back in at a pace you can handle. Check back in please, you are worthy, needed and missed.

Day 21

There are businesses, institutions, and organizations that make lots of money when you do not take care of yourself. You can care for yourself and others. It just takes the support and guidance sometimes. You don't have to let shame or embarrassment force you into doing it alone.

Day 22

Take it one day at a time. Participation not Perfection is the goal.

Day 23

Get a Self Care Buddy who encourages you, reminds you to be gentle with yourself and laughs with you.

Day 24

It only takes a few moments to care for yourself. Take just one moment now and build on what you already are doing.

Day 25

Ask for help with one Self Care Goal today.

Day 26

The look of joy a person who has been hurting gets after receiving something they critically need is truly unforgettable. Create that look of joy for yourself by asking for help today.

Day 27

Write down or tell someone what a Self Care Day would look like for you. Call your Self Care Buddy today.

Day 28

When living out your purpose to serve others, you could easily run yourself in the ground... which doesn't serve them for long. You will become less than a help, you will become their heartbreak. Take care of yourself. Take a Self Care Baby Step today.

Day 29

Helping others becomes an excellent emotional self-care act when you are not using it to cover up a critical state you are in. The blessings of giving are always sweetest when you are able to give while caring for your own critical needs at the same time. Do a little something today to address a critical need you have while still helping others.

Day 30

Celebrate your self-care choices made by continuing to ask for help.

10 Revolutionary Self Care Strategies

To help HEAL Black Lives

1. **Take time daily to discover and review what you *critically* need in every self-care category.** *Action*: Ask "What do I critically need today?" If you don't know, ask for help and guidance

2. **Acknowledge the healing benefits of being physically around those who love black people the way you love black people.** *Action*: Research activities and events you do not organize yourself that hold the space for the celebration of being black without the ridicule.

3. **Develop and keep in touch with your own personal Self Care Dream Team.** *Action*: Write the names and numbers down of those who have wisdom and actually care about how you are caring for

yourself in each of the self-care categories. Call them. Ask for guidance every time you need it. You can have more than one.

4. **Incorporate regular self-care check-ins with your family, friends and organizing groups.** *Action*: Contact via email, social media, phone or in person those who are familiar with a Self Care Plan and ask them to be a Self Care Buddy to check in with you every now and then. Do not psycho analyze each other just listen.

5. **Welcome the artistic and cultural healing tools like dance, visual arts, spoken word and live music to be a part of your monthly self-care strategy.** *Action*: Locate the centers and organizations in your community that offer artistic and cultural gatherings. You do not have to talk to anyone to benefit. Just sit back and absorb. When you are ready to you can participate.

6. **Enact one Self Care Baby Step a Day.**
   Action: Ask yourself "What would seem to
   be an absurdly simple act that would get me
   closer to my Self Care Goal today?" Write it
   down or do it for one or all of the categories.

7. **Read books, watch videos and talk to
   those who have loved, encouraged
   and led black people to understand
   their personal self-care strategies.**
   Action: Ask "How do you take care of
   yourself after watching a shooting video or
   after learning the depth of our problems as
   a people?"

8. **Learn the totality of our people's
   history so this very moment does not
   define what you think about yourself
   or our people**. *Action*: Refresh your
   memory on the many global
   representations of our people who have
   healed themselves, governed themselves
   and protected themselves. Feed your soul

with their triumphs because they are a part of you. This is a form of educational, spiritual, social and emotional self-care.

9. **Layer the way you address your critical self-care needs.** *Action*: If someone invites you to a meeting, inquire if food will be present you can eat. When needing to address community issues, be sure to incorporate as many of your other critical self care needs at the same time as possible. It is OK to take a break and fuel up. You being healthy is us winning.

10. **Join an organization.** *Action:* Research and "date" organizations before you get married. It has been said "isolation breeds illness". For you to feel empowered and healing sooner, join forces with those who can amplify your revolutionary actions. If you are already a member of an organization, contact the sistercarealliance.org and we can help you become trained to establish the first Self Care Support Group for your organization's members. Every organization should house one regularly.

About the Author

 Anana Harris Parris is the Director of Operations and Community Affairs for the Davis Bozeman Law Firm, founder of the AfriSalsa Cultural Organization, the AfriSalsa fights HIV/AIDS Campaign, the SisterCARE Alliance and the Self Care Day Campaign. As the Director of Operations and Community Affairs, Ms. Parris oversees all internal operations, the internship program and the Community Affairs Division at DB Law. Ms. Parris is responsible for organizing collaborative community projects such as: "Respect Black Life: I am Trayvon Martin March" of over 5000 marchers from Atlanta University Center to the CNN Center, "Remembrance March for Charleston Victims", the Self Care Matters Tour and the New Beginnings Re-entry Mentoring Program in partnership with the Urban League, Morehouse School of Medicine and the U.S. Attorney General's Office of Northern District of Georgia.

Anana Harris Parris, born in Washington D.C., was raised by culturally rich and socially active parents from New Roads and Jennings, Louisiana who encouraged success in her career and community as a priority. While living in Washington D.C. as a student at Howard University, Ms. Parris worked as the Implementation and Marketing Coordinator for an international telecommunications company called Swisscom North America where she learned the art of Marketing and internal workflow implementation. Ms. Parris also coordinated a monthly socio-political discussion and dance event titled "The Community Gatherings" and began a dance career as a performing member of the Balafon West African Dance Ensemble. Ms. Parris forged a consulting career grounded in community conscious business enhancement. Ms. Parris accepted an offer to become the Chief Operating Officer and co-owner of the GTM Agency in June of 2000 in Atlanta, Ga. Ms. Parris established the operating structure of the startup company as well as the logistic operational design for their largest account, a 26 city national promotion of the Truth™ anti-tobacco campaign. Through the Truth Campaign, she was able to learn the power and technique of cause based brand marketing, innovative business plan modeling and gained invaluable experience with multilevel operations management.

In 2004, Ms. Parris launched the AfriSalsa Cultural Organization and the AfriSalsa™ fights HIV/AIDS Campaign which used cultural dance as a creative public health educational medium through interactive workshops and presentations. This unique approach to public health education through the cultural arts was highlighted in the internationally acclaimed documentary "The AIDS Chronicles". Through AfriSalsa, Ms. Parris has worked to raise awareness and funds for those in need with organizations such as AID Atlanta, Taller Portobello Norte, A Lotus Legacy Foundation, the ALAFIA Project at Emory School of Medicine and Atlanta Salsa Community Haitian Earthquake Relief Efforts among others. Ms. Parris has also spread her love of cultural education through dance. As a dancer, instructor and choreographer for Atlanta based dance companies such as Giwayen Mata, Proyecto Barrio, Injabulo Leta and The Alaje Group, Ms. Parris has performed in many traditional dance styles including Guinean, South African, AfroCuban and AfriSalsa Fusion.

In 2011, Ms. Parris authored the first official Self Care Day Proclamation on behalf of the AfriSalsa Cultural Organization which is recognized on December 4th to promote self-care through community activism and the arts. The purpose of establishing Self Care Days is make self-care a topic of political discussions and direct funding to those experiencing depression, bullying, domestic abuse, injustices, recovery from trauma and other social ills. Currently Self Care Day is recognized in the cities of Atlanta, Savannah and Lithonia, Georgia as well as DeKalb County through the SisterCARE Alliance. Increasing interest in the Self Care Day Campaign, led to the development of the SisterCARE Alliance initiative founded by Ms. Parris in 2014. SisterCARE Alliance is a women's empowerment network that promotes self-care and social activism to its members and educates women and girls of color on critical self-care strategies.

Ms. Parris' mission to promote the revolutionary impact of self-care through programming and products also birthed the social enterprise The Self Care Agency. Through The Self Care Agency, Ms. Parris launched workshops including the Self Care Matters Intensive Program, Self Care for Work-Life Balance, interactive "AfriSalsa's Salsa for Self Care" workshops and many more. Speaking regularly to young women groups and professional organizations, Ms. Parris has had the pleasure of partnering with institutions and businesses such as 100 Black Women of DeKalb County/ Decatur, Carol's Daughter, the Jimmy Carter Center, New Rock Legal Society and more. In addition to providing impactful self-care based products and services, The Self Care Agency in partnership with the SisterCARE Alliance provides support services, presentations and self-care program training to battered women's shelters, youth detention centers, pregnant teen programs and the often forgotten everyday working professional. To fund this community focused effort, the Self Care Agency offers products including a nutraceutical supplement system called Kyani, Self Care Soaps and Scrubs, Self Care Instructional Manuals and Self Care Thoughts Audio Recordings.

As a result of her many years of volunteering and community service, Ms. Parris was selected as a delegate to represent the City of Atlanta at the Global Peace Foundation's Annual Conference and has also received several awards. Ms. Parris was awarded the Unsung Heroine Award of 2012 by the National Coalition of 100 Black Women, Inc., the Red Cross Hurricane Katrina Community Service Award, and The Soul Dance & Artist Grief Advocate Award from Project Karma, Inc. and the U.S. Attorney General's Office Community Outreach Award of 2014. Most recently in March of 2016, Ms. Parris was honored at the Georgia State Capitol and awarded the title of Goodwill Ambassador for the State of Georgia for her work around community affairs, self-care and cross cultural education.

It is through her passion for her community, key involvement with socially impactful organizations like the Davis Bozeman Law Firm and the prayers of her great grandparents that propel Ms. Parris forward.

Thank you Mama and Daddy.

The journey of becoming a parent is challenging. To add a civil rights movement and racism to the journey of a parent fighting to create children with a love of who they are and where they come from almost seems impossible. But my parents chose to anyway. Being a parent and having a family that loves each other and loves the skin and culture they are in is a revolutionary triumph that comes at a high price. Thank you mama and daddy for paying that price for us.

Thank you mama for carrying me, loving me and giving me the gift of dance while still fighting as an activist for our people. Your heart has always shown through. I see your love. Through you mama, I have learned what compassion really is.

Daddy, you help me feel stronger, worthy and loved. You remind me every day I am not just some random woman out here in the world. I am Anana. Having you in my corner has been the saving grace of my darkest hour. Thank you daddy for showing me and teaching me what courage really is.

About This Book

Self Care Matters: A Revolutionary's Approach First Edition is the inaugural text written by Anana Johari Harris Parris outlining, why self-care is revolutionary and how to develop your own Self Care Plan. It includes topic discussions on:

- How to Create a Self Care Strategy
- Self Care Barriers
- Personal Stories of Self Care Journeys from the Author
- How to Start Your Own Self Care Support Group
- Perspectives of Self Care from women, men, mothers, business owners and community activists
- A Social Justice Perspective on Self Care
and more...

For those self-care advocates, ambassadors and leaders in their communities needing a framework for serving others that incorporates practical self-care principles, this book is for you. For natural givers that want to continue giving without running themselves in the ground, this book is for you. For those in a business or personal relationship with someone that has poor self-care habits, this book is for you. Givers, community leaders and care takers hold up the critical areas of our society. We need you most desperately to continue on as your healthiest self.

Made in the USA
San Bernardino, CA
26 November 2018